GENES &
THE
LIFE PROCESS

GENES &
THE
LIFE PROCESS

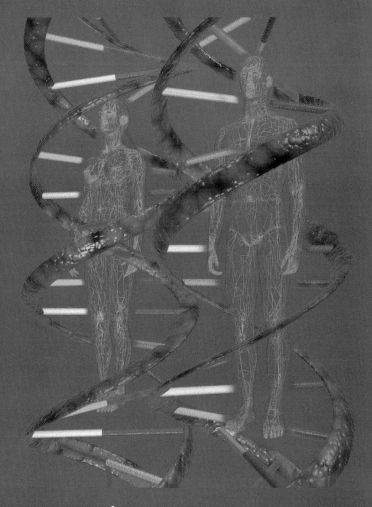

 Reader's Digest

The Reader's Digest Association Limited
London New York Sydney Montreal

Genes and the Life Process

was created and produced by
Carroll & Brown Limited
20 Lonsdale Road
London NW6 6RD
for Reader's Digest, London

ISBN 0 276 42880 3

Reproduced by Colour Systems, London
Printed and bound in the EEC by
Arvato Iberia

The information in this book is for reference only; it is not intended as a substitute for a doctor's diagnosis and care. The editors urge anyone with continuing medical problems or symptoms to consult a doctor.

Managing editor
Anne Yelland

Managing art editor
Anne Fisher

Editors
Judy Fovargue, Marianne Canty

Art editors
Vimit Punater, Justin Ford

Series medical consultant
Dr Lesley Hickin, MB BS, BSc, DRCOG, MRCGP, General Practitioner

Genetics specialist consultant
Stewart J Payne, BSc, DipRCPath, Head of Molecular Genetics Laboratory,
North West Thames Regional Genetics Service, Northwick Park Hospital, Harrow

CONTRIBUTORS

Wynnie Chan, BSc, PhD, Public Health Nutritionist

Christel Edwards-de Graauw, Nail Technician, Nail Artist and Makeup Artist,
Fingernails Direct, Northern Ireland

Chrissie Gallagher-Mundy, BA (Hons), Fitness Writer, Director,
London Academy of Personal Fitness

Leslie Colvin James, MSc, CGC, Genetic Counselor, Instructor, Department of Genetics,
Louisiana State University Health Sciences Center, New Orleans

Joel Levy, BSc, MA, Medical Writer

Brice Pitt, MD, FRCPsych, Emeritus Professor, Psychiatry of Old Age,
Imperial College. London

Penny Preston, MB, ChB, MRCGP, Medical Writer

Rona Slator, DPhil, FRCS (Plast), Consultant Plastic Surgeon,
Birmingham Children's Hospital

Dr Michael Spira, MB BS, MRCS, LRCP, General Practitioner

For Reader's Digest
Series Editor Christine Noble
Art Editor Julie Bennett
Reader's Digest General Books
Editorial Director Cortina Butler
Art Director Nick Clark

Genes and the Life Process

Awareness of health issues and expectations of medicine are greater today than ever before. A long and healthy life has come to be looked on as not so much a matter of luck but as almost a right. However, as our knowledge of health and the causes of disease has grown, it has become increasingly clear that health is something that we can all influence, for better or worse, through choices we make in our lives. *Your Body Your Health* is designed to help you make the right choices to make the most of your health potential. Each volume in the series focuses on a different physiological system of the body, explaining what it does and how it works. There is a wealth of advice and health tips on diet, exercise and lifestyle factors, as well as the health checks you can expect throughout life. You will find out what can go wrong and what can be done about it, and learn from people's real-life experiences of diagnosis and treatment. Finally, there is a detailed A to Z index of the major conditions which can affect the system. The series builds into a complete user's manual for the care and maintenance of the entire body.

This volume looks at the tiniest building blocks of life – genes and the DNA that exists inside every cell in your body. Part I explains what they are and how, quite literally, they make you who you are – the product of your parents and their DNA, and absolutely unique (unless, of course, you are an identical twin). Your genetic inheritance influences every stage of your life, from the moment of conception until you die, and here you will read how lifestyle choices can affect whether an inherited tendency becomes a health problem. As scientists unravel the genetic code, they are learning more about individual risks of health problems and what can be done to prevent these risks from adversely affecting quality of life. We introduce the genetic specialists, and explain the tests and treatments that have been developed so far for disorders with a genetic component. And you will also read of the tantalising possibilities for future gene manipulation to treat or prevent disorders which were once considered life-threatening.

Contents

3

What happens when things go wrong

The natural history of the life cycle

The changing form and faculties of a human being progressing through life have attracted the attention of many of the world's greatest thinkers. Today, in the era of biotechnology and molecular genetics, we know more than ever before about the complex processes that underlie the human life cycle, and the extraordinary pathways that led it to evolve as it did.

When sperm were first viewed with the earliest microscopes, it was believed that each one carried a tiny homunculus, a person formed in perfect miniature, which would take root in a woman's womb and there grow in size until it emerged nine months later. Now we know that the man's sperm must fertilise the woman's egg and that from this single fertilised egg, just 0.1mm wide, a new human being develops. From single merged cell to fully grown fetus requires a mindblowing 1000 trillion cell divisions.

BLOODLINES
Our ideas about the forces that direct and control the life cycle have also changed. In medieval times it was believed that the traits and characteristics that a person developed during their life came down to them through the mixing of their parental bloodlines – that hereditary information was literally carried in the blood. Ironically we now know that, since they have no nucleus, red blood cells are the only cells in the human body that do not carry hereditary information. White blood cells, on the other hand, were where the true home of genetics and the hereditary

principle was discovered, because DNA was first isolated from pus, the build-up of white blood cells that occurs around a wound or infection. This feat was accomplished in 1869 by a young Swiss chemist, Johann Friedrich Miescher, working with pus-soaked bandages from a nearby hospital. He named the product he isolated nucleic acid. However, it was to be nearly a century before the significance of what we now know as deoxyribonucleic acid (DNA) was appreciated.

MENDEL'S PEAS
Shortly before Miescher discovered DNA, an Austrian monk, Gregor Mendel, had published a paper outlining his experiments with pea plants. In these experiments Mendel had discovered some important principles underlying the way that traits such as seed shape and colour – he isolated seven main traits in all – were inherited between one

A human being has around 32,000 genes, included within a total of some 6.6 billion or more units of DNA.

Unravelling the structure of DNA
Rosalind Franklin (below) was the first to succeed in taking X-rays of DNA, which revealed a great deal about its structure. Crick and Watson (right) used this information to build a model of the double helix, after working out how the base pairs fitted together.

generation and the next. In particular, he had deduced that the traits must be determined by what he called discrete hereditary particles – units of hereditary information that today are known as genes.

A NEW DAWN FOR BIOLOGY

Mendel's momentous discovery went largely unnoticed at the time, but in 1900 three other scientists reached the same conclusion and set in motion one of the most exciting scientific pursuits of modern times: to discover where in the cell genes are stored, and which molecule is used to encode them. Research teams in America and Europe vied to become the first to identify this all-important molecule and then to explain how it worked.

EYES ON THE PRIZE

While researchers such as Oswald Avery and Thomas Hunt Morgan, working in America, claimed the honours for identifying DNA as the hereditary principle and discovering the role of chromosomes in the hereditary process, the ultimate accolade was to go to a pair of young scientists working in Britain, who achieved their goal without performing a single experiment. In 1953, in a short letter to the science journal *Nature*, Francis Crick and James Watson, basing their work on research carried out at King's College in London, set out the structure of DNA and explained how it contained and passed on the genetic code that forms the basis for all life on Earth. The Nobel Prize and a place in the history books were theirs, and the new understanding of how the life cycle is controlled by genes opened the doors to new sciences and raised new hopes for medicine, agriculture and many other fields.

EVOLVING THE LIFE CYCLE

The discovery of genes and DNA has also allowed scientists to follow the evolutionary development of the human life cycle in unprecedented detail, tracing its history back through the eras to the very beginning of life on Earth. We know that all living organisms share the same basic genetic mechanisms, and furthermore, that we share many genes with creatures far distant from us in the tree of life. Many of these genes have survived almost unaltered through aeons of time, like fossils preserved in our own genetic makeup.

Among these ancient survivors are many of the genes that oversee the human life cycle, including those that guide fetal development, pubertal change and eventual senescence – the final stage of life. But though the genes themselves may not have changed much, evolution has tinkered significantly with the way they are deployed in humans, to give the human life cycle several strange and unique features.

INVENTING CHILDHOOD

The infancy and childhood stages of the human life cycle are extremely unusual among vertebrates and certainly do not match those of our closest primate relatives. Our infancy period is characterised by total helplessness and intense physical and neurological development, while childhood is an entirely human invention.

PREMATURE BIRTH

When a chimpanzee or gorilla baby is born, it is fairly capable compared to a human baby. All of its bones – even its fingers and toes – have already started to ossify (the process whereby their cartilage is replaced by hard, bony material), and its rate of brain growth has slowed compared to the rate during fetal growth. The brain of a human baby, on the other hand, continues to grow at an incredible rate, exactly as if it were still in the womb, and at birth some of a baby's bones are also still in a 'fetal' state. A human baby does not reach the same state of growth as an ape baby at birth until the age of 12 months, so that the first year or so of human infancy closely resembles an extended fetal stage. In other words, the true length of human gestation is about 21 months, except that most of it happens outside the womb.

Mother and baby
Orang utan mothers and their infants are inseparable until the young are weaned around the age of five. The offspring then enter a period of adolescence, with females becoming sexually mature at the age of seven. Males mature two years later. There is no equivalent of childhood among the great apes.

Helpless newborn
*Human babies are born completely
helpless. They must be fed, kept warm
and protected from external threats
not for months but years.*

HUMAN LIFE

Arguments over the relative
effects of genetics and
environment on human life
may rage, but are largely
irrelevant to the fact that the
human life cycle is unique:
human life features distinct
stages which are not shared
by even our closest relatives.

INFANCY

CHILDHOOD

Learning fast
*Weaning comes fast to human children.
Chimpanzees and gorillas breastfeed their
young approximately six times as long as
their period of gestation: this would indicate
a 'natural' weaning age for humans of four
and a half years.*

A unique stage?
*At birth, the ratio of brain weight to body
weight in apes and humans is similar, but by
adulthood a human's brain is more than
three times heavier than an ape's. Scientists
suggest that this growth is one of the reasons
for the prolonged stage of human childhood.*

This extended fetal period probably developed because
the female pelvis is too narrow to accommodate the head
of a 21-month-old baby. To be safely born, humans have
evolved a trade off where they complete fetal development
outside the womb. This also allows for the human baby's
brain to develop in a rich sensory environment, helping to
produce a higher level of intelligence.

THE NEW GENERATION
In apes infancy ends with weaning, after which comes the
juvenile stage, when the young ape can just about look
after itself. In humans, however, there is a unique extra
stage that comes between the infant and juvenile stages –
childhood. During childhood the human digestive system

and teeth are still not fully mature while continued brain
growth means that children need a high-energy diet. To
meet these demands, children remain dependent on adults,
even after weaning, hence the need for this stage of the
human life cycle. Childhood also provides an environment
where training can shape the brain, enhancing intelligence.

LIFE CHANGES
Unusual features of the human life cycle do not end with
childhood. The transitional stage of puberty has been
compared to the radical metamorphosis undergone by
insects and amphibians, while menopause may be another
unique human feature. Why would human females have
evolved such an abrupt end to their reproductive

Finding the trigger
Scientists still don't know what causes the hypothalamus to start releasing the hormones that trigger puberty. Hormones, the nervous system, and factors such as diet, are all believed to be involved.

The end of fertility
In other mammals, female reproductive capability starts to fail at about the same time as other body systems, so that females can bear young almost until they die. Humans are unique in ending female fertility up to 50 years before death.

MENOPAUSE

OLD AGE

PUBERTY

All change at puberty
Before puberty, girls and boys have the same muscle and skeletal mass and body weight. Adult men have 1.5 times the skeletal and muscle mass of women, but women have twice as much body fat.

A ripe old age
Scientists have succeeded in identifying the genes which control ageing in worms, and have found similar genes in humans. It seems unlikely, however, that the end of life will be dramatically prolonged in the near future.

potential? One theory is that as humans began to live longer, there came a time when it was a better allocation of a female's energy to help raise grandchildren rather than risk the dangers of childbirth again.

THE RIDDLE OF AGEING

The final phase of the human life cycle is old age, or senescence. Most creatures have a senescent phase, but not all. Some types of fish, for instance, simply keep on growing until they die. Why don't humans? One speculation is that preventing ageing means constantly repairing the damage that the body and its cells accumulate, which takes a lot of energy. Humans have a

finite energy metabolism and evolution favours those who expend a fair proportion on reproduction and child-raising over those who conserve their energy for self-repair. It makes more evolutionary sense to live fast and die young, so long as you leave behind descendants.

IT DIDN'T HAVE TO BE YOU

All of us follow a similar life cycle, but the mysteries of heredity determine that each individual life cycle is utterly unique. Out of all the possible combinations of genome that your parents could have produced by combining their gametes, the odds that yours would be the one that resulted are around 1 in 3 billion. And if one of those

DNA in the human genome is arranged into 23 pairs of chromosomes, which range in length from about 50 million to 260 million base pairs. A difference in just one base pair on a chromosome can result in an abnormality.

3 billion alternatives had been the result, it too would have been unique. Your genome is yours alone, as is the pattern of events that it sets in train and then guides it through the years.

AN OPEN BOOK

The advent of genetics means that it is now increasingly possible to read the book of life represented by the genome, and from it to glean vital health hints for each stage of the life cycle. This process can begin even before birth, thanks to prenatal testing, which can reveal the presence of serious congenital diseases and defects. Routine tests performed at birth include genetic tests for diseases such as phenylketonuria, a disorder resulting from a defect in a single gene, which used to be fatal to all children born with it but can now be treated through diet.

Genetic testing can help to diagnose diseases and disorders that become apparent during childhood and later life, while screening techniques and genetic counselling can help parents to assess their risks of passing on a problem gene to their offspring and prevent it. As we learn more about the genetics of problems such as heart disease, cancer and osteoporosis, it will become increasingly possible to screen for susceptibilities and target preventative and therapeutic measures towards those who need them.

Practically all aspects of medicine can benefit from a genetic perspective, from pharmaceuticals to surgery. The first 'gene chips' for drug response testing have been produced. These use samples from a patient's DNA, fixed onto a sort of microchip, to test a patient's likely response to a medicine and adjust doses to suit. In the near future research teams hope to produce genetically modified organs and tissues that can be used for transplants and grafting without being rejected by the recipient's immune system.

TINKERING WITH THE FUTURE

In the future the science of genetics may have an even greater impact on our life cycle. Gene therapy holds the promise of cures for ills at all stages of life, while advances in our knowledge of the genetics of ageing may one day offer the possibility of a longer lifespan. It may even be possible to engineer specific traits and characteristics to produce so-called designer babies or change people's bodies according to fashion.

Such possibilities raise important moral as well as scientific issues. On the threshold of a new era of medicine and biology, it has never been more important to understand the nature and working of your amazing genes, and how they govern and influence your life cycle.

The future for genes
Scientists at the Imperial Cancer Research Fund are using gene therapy in the fight against skin cancer. Cells coloured blue have the cancer gene switched on; those coloured yellow are healthy, with the gene switched off. The aim is to harness the genetic switch to express an anti-cancer gene to help to destroy cancer cells.

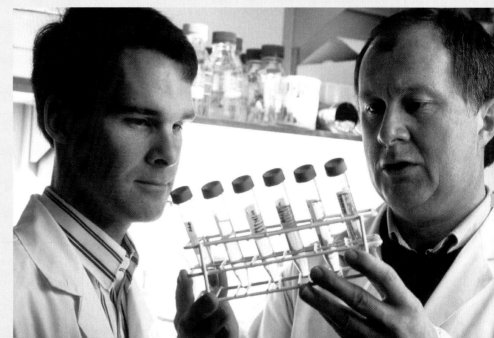

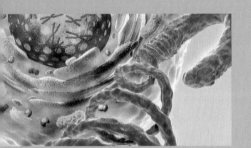  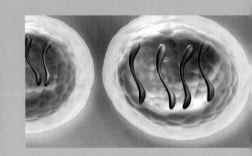

1

How your genes work

Genes and the life cycle

From conception to death, the development, workings and destiny of each and every cell in your body is controlled by the interplay between the genetic information stored in your DNA and the world around you.

THE MUSIC OF LIFE

Early philosophers and scientists knew that heredity was important. They knew that certain traits ran in families and that children inherited physical and mental characteristics from their parents. Few of them, however, could have guessed just how important heredity really is.

At the dawn of the third millennium, the relatively young science of genetics is revealing more and more of the code that lies in the core of every cell of your body, and discovering that it controls or influences almost every aspect of human biology, psychology and behaviour. This code is the DNA sequence that makes up your genome – your genetic inheritance. Like the score for a rich and complex symphony, your genome spells out the music of your life.

But researchers have also discovered that there is much more to this symphony than just its score, because the genetic instructions contained in your DNA do not exist in a vacuum. They are expressed in living cells in a body that exists in an ever-changing and unpredictable world. The music of your life is really the music of chance as well as the inherited symphony. Genes and environment work together to produce a final outcome and you have the power to shape your own environment: if your genes are the score, you are the conductor.

Cytoplasm *surrounds and protects the cell nucleus and is the site of DNA replication (see pages 22–23).*

The nucleus *of the cell is where our genes are stored on chromosomes.*

From little acorns
It's a long way from the sequence of molecules that spell out a genetic code to a living human being. On pages 30–31, you can find out how genes direct fetal development, differentiating top from bottom, left from right and back from front, and instructing particular cells to grow into particular organs.

Childhood development
As children, we develop intelligence and personality. We enjoy some foods but dislike others, and we learn to interact with carers and peers. Some children may have inherited problems – find out how this happens on pages 22–23. How and why genes are involved in their passage from childhood to adulthood is explained on pages 32–33.

Heart of the matter

With the notable exception of red blood cells, the nucleus of every cell that goes to make up the human body contains a copy of the genome. This is the genetic code that governs everything from eye colour to when and how a person might die. The cell nucleus organises and stores genes in chromosomes and allows DNA – from which genes and chromosomes are composed – replication. The cell nucleus is surrounded and protected by jellylike cytoplasm.

Chromosomes – gene carriers

In the heart of each cell the genetic material is collected into structures known as chromosomes. Humans have 46 chromosomes arranged into 23 pairs. In 22 of these pairs the chromosomes look identical, but the last pair, known as the sex chromosomes, can be different. If they are both large, x-shaped chromosomes, known as X chromosomes, the bearer is female. If only one is an X chromosome and the other is a smaller Y chromosome, the bearer is male.

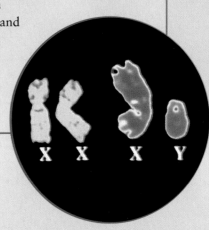

X   X   X   Y

Chromosomes – *each X shape represents a matched pair of chromosomes, one from each parent.*

When I'm 64

How will you look when you are older? How much hair will you have? Will you develop a life-threatening illness, such as heart disease or Alzheimer's? The genes that determine the answers to these questions and those that are responsible for the ageing of cells are explored on pages 28–29 and 38–39.

All grown up

As adults, we select partners, have children, forge careers, follow interests – and sometimes develop diseases. All of these things are influenced to some extent by our genes. See pages 36–37 and 38–39 to find out more.

Humans are 98 per cent genetically identical to chimpanzees – that's a smaller difference than that between chimps and gorillas.

Genes and DNA

For many years scientists searched cells for the substance that carried inherited characteristics. What they found was astonishingly simple, and shared by all life on Earth.

WHAT ARE GENES?

A gene is a unit of hereditary information, an instruction to an organism telling it to make something or have a certain characteristic. In humans, for instance, one gene makes people blood type A, while a slightly different version makes people blood type B. Often several genes contribute to determining a characteristic. Potential height, for instance, is determined by the action of several genes at once – a multifactorial characteristic. Collectively, your complement of genes adds up to your genome. Most of the genes in your genome are the same as every other human's: in fact you share a large number with most other organisms on the planet.

A gene is essentially a piece of information but this has to be coded and stored in some physical way in order to be used, copied and passed on. For many years scientists searched for the molecule that fulfilled this role. Eventually they discovered it inside the nucleus of each cell.

CRACKING THE CODE

Inside each cell's nucleus is a quantity of deoxyribonucleic acid (DNA), and it is this that carries your genetic information in the form of a code. The nature of the code is simple yet ingenious, and it is determined by the molecular structure and makeup of the DNA in base pairs.

The base pairs code for proteins, or more precisely, for the sequence of amino acids that make up a protein. Since, in humans, there are 20 possible amino acids, the DNA code contains at least 20 different 'codons' – units of information each specifying a different amino acid.

There are four different bases which can make up the 'letters' of a codon. If the minimum length of a codon was two letters or bases, there would only be 16 possible combinations, not enough to code for 20 amino acids. The minimum length of each codon is, therefore, three bases (a codon is also known as a triplet for this reason). This gives 64 possible codons, 60 of which code for amino acids (more than one codon is needed to produce some amino acids), one is a 'start' signal and the other three are 'stop' signals.

If all the DNA in a single cell was stretched out to its full length it would stand a metre high.

Coils upon coils
Normally the DNA in the nucleus of a cell is spread out and invisible even under a microscope. When a cell is preparing to divide, however, the DNA helix coils up into thicker strands, which then coil up themselves until they are wound up into the arms of a chromosome.

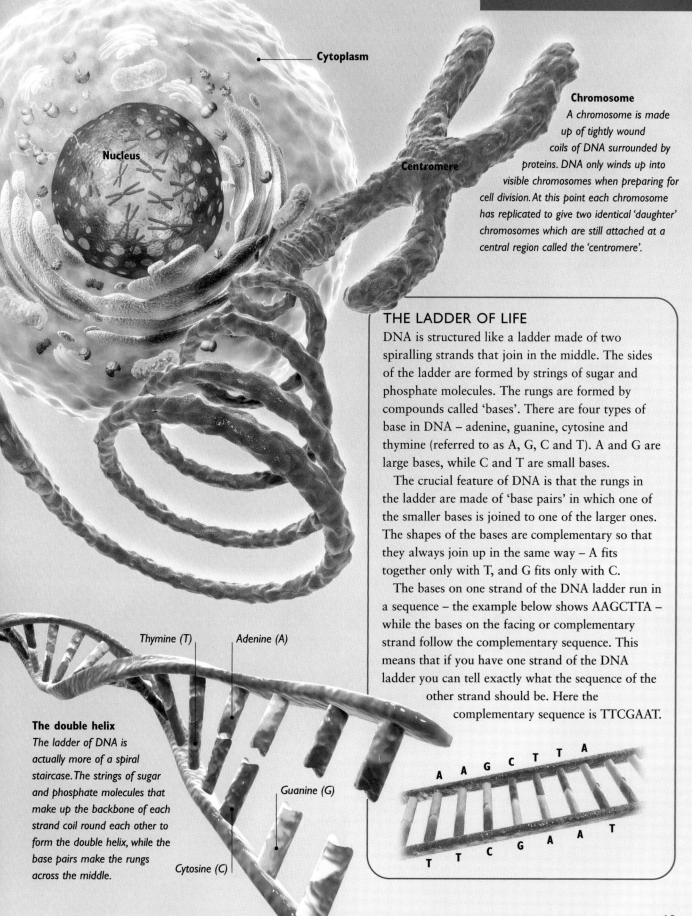

Cytoplasm

Chromosome
*A chromosome is made
up of tightly wound
coils of DNA surrounded by
proteins. DNA only winds up into
visible chromosomes when preparing for
cell division. At this point each chromosome
has replicated to give two identical 'daughter'
chromosomes which are still attached at a
central region called the 'centromere'.*

Nucleus

Centromere

THE LADDER OF LIFE

DNA is structured like a ladder made of two
spiralling strands that join in the middle. The sides
of the ladder are formed by strings of sugar and
phosphate molecules. The rungs are formed by
compounds called 'bases'. There are four types of
base in DNA – adenine, guanine, cytosine and
thymine (referred to as A, G, C and T). A and G are
large bases, while C and T are small bases.

   The crucial feature of DNA is that the rungs in
the ladder are made of 'base pairs' in which one of
the smaller bases is joined to one of the larger ones.
The shapes of the bases are complementary so that
they always join up in the same way – A fits
together only with T, and G fits only with C.

   The bases on one strand of the DNA ladder run in
a sequence – the example below shows AAGCTTA –
while the bases on the facing or complementary
strand follow the complementary sequence. This
means that if you have one strand of the DNA
ladder you can tell exactly what the sequence of the
other strand should be. Here the
complementary sequence is TTCGAAT.

Thymine (T)   Adenine (A)

Guanine (G)

The double helix
*The ladder of DNA is
actually more of a spiral
staircase. The strings of sugar
and phosphate molecules that
make up the backbone of each
strand coil round each other to
form the double helix, while the
base pairs make the rungs
across the middle.*

Cytosine (C)

A A G C T T A

T T C G A A T

From genes to proteins

Your DNA sequence is information, pure and simple. It takes the machinery of the cell's molecular biology to translate this information into structure and action.

The cell nucleus
Transcription takes place in the nucleus: DNA is only found in the nucleus.

Amino acid attached to piece of tRNA

GENE PRODUCTS

Your genes are expressed through the proteins that are made according to their DNA instructions. Proteins are versatile molecules. Some become structural elements such as keratin, which makes up hair and nails, or myosin, a component of muscle fibres. Some become biological catalysts called enzymes, which help to construct or break down other types of molecule. Pepsin, for example, is an enzyme that helps your digestive system to break down proteins in your food. Other types of protein become messengers, receptors and signals.

TRANSCRIPTION AND TRANSLATION

The process by which a DNA sequence leads to the production of a protein has two parts: transcription and translation. In transcription, copies of the DNA sequence of a gene are made using a nucleic acid called RNA. This is closely related to DNA, sharing the same structure of bases attached to a sugar-phosphate backbone. DNA is copied into messenger RNA (mRNA) which then passes out of the nucleus into the cytoplasm for translation.

In translation, the strand of mRNA is used as a template for the construction of a string of amino acids. The mRNA moves through a protein-assembly unit called a ribosome, selecting the relevant amino acids to match each of its codons. Amino acids are delivered on short lengths of another type of RNA, called transfer RNA (tRNA) – tRNAs are also produced in the nucleus and transported out to the cytoplasm to work on protein production. tRNa molecules have a characteristic 'clover-leaf' structure. The amino acid is attached to the 'stem' of the leaf. Three key bases in the central leaf of the structure are complementary to the codon on the mRNA template specific to the particular amino acid carried by the tRNA. These three bases on the tRNA are called anticodons and each anticodon will only match with its complementary codon on the mRNA message. As the mRNA moves through the ribosome, successive tRNAs match with the correct sequence of triplet codons on the mRNA and bring in their attached amino acids which are joined into a chain that will eventually become the finished protein.

TRANSCRIPTION

1 The DNA helix untwists and the strands separate so that one side can be used as the template for the manufacture of a strand of mRNA.

2 Unattached bases float by – if they match the exposed bases on the DNA they are grabbed and joined together to build up the mRNA strand. This all takes place in the nucleus.

THE FINAL FOLDING

When the ribosome comes to a 'stop' codon, it disengages from the mRNA strand and starts work on another strand. Meanwhile, the positive or negative charge of the completed amino acid chain causes the chain to twist and fold. Sometimes several separate chains must be joined to create the final protein – haemoglobin, for example, is made of four chains. The folding stage is crucial as the final shape of the protein dictates its special function and abilities. A third of proteins are destroyed within minutes of manufacture because they are not the right shape.

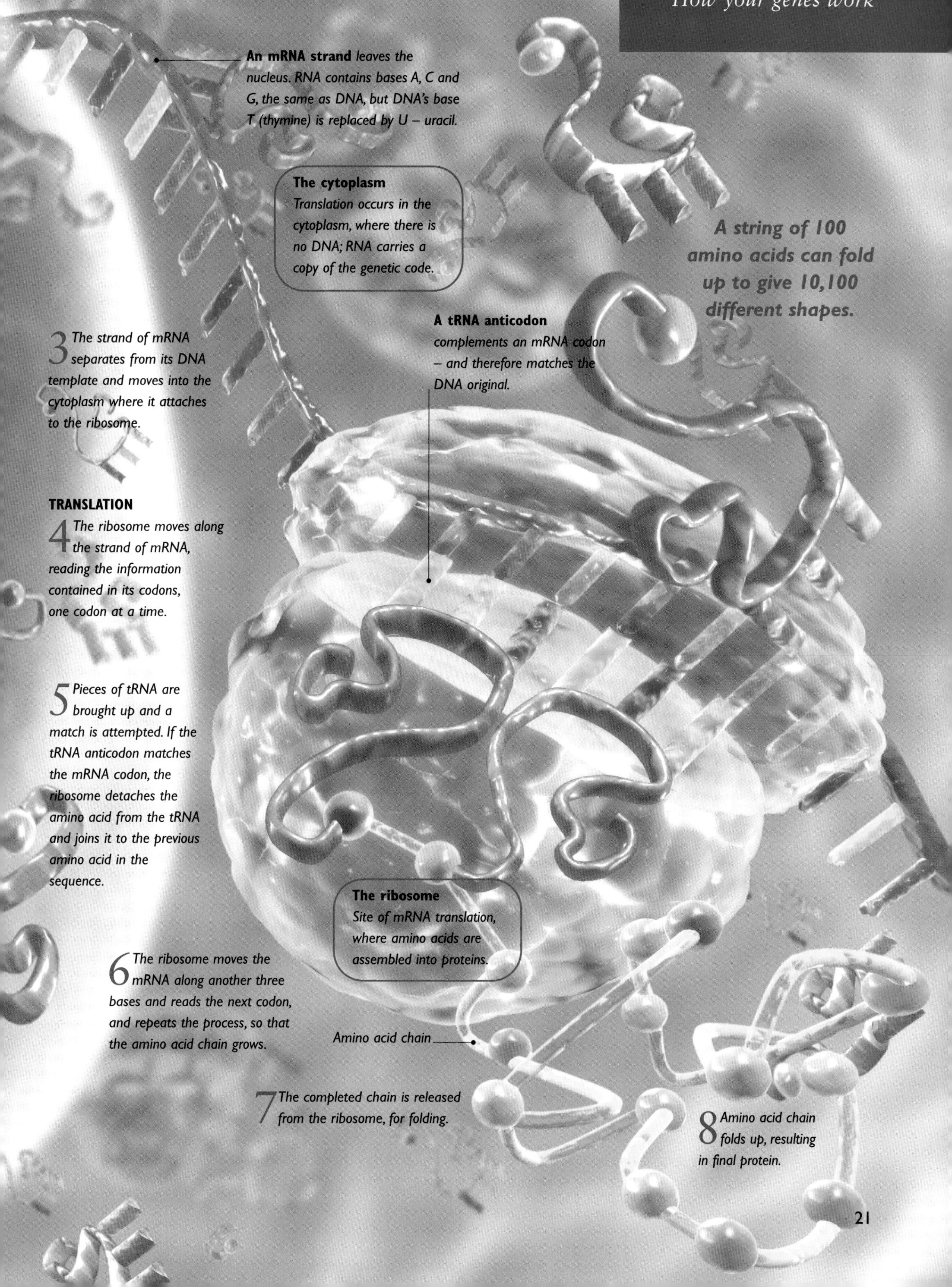

An mRNA strand *leaves the nucleus. RNA contains bases A, C and G, the same as DNA, but DNA's base T (thymine) is replaced by U – uracil.*

The cytoplasm
Translation occurs in the cytoplasm, where there is no DNA; RNA carries a copy of the genetic code.

A tRNA anticodon
complements an mRNA codon – and therefore matches the DNA original.

A string of 100 amino acids can fold up to give 10,100 different shapes.

3 *The strand of mRNA separates from its DNA template and moves into the cytoplasm where it attaches to the ribosome.*

TRANSLATION

4 *The ribosome moves along the strand of mRNA, reading the information contained in its codons, one codon at a time.*

5 *Pieces of tRNA are brought up and a match is attempted. If the tRNA anticodon matches the mRNA codon, the ribosome detaches the amino acid from the tRNA and joins it to the previous amino acid in the sequence.*

The ribosome
Site of mRNA translation, where amino acids are assembled into proteins.

6 *The ribosome moves the mRNA along another three bases and reads the next codon, and repeats the process, so that the amino acid chain grows.*

Amino acid chain

7 *The completed chain is released from the ribosome, for folding.*

8 *Amino acid chain folds up, resulting in final protein.*

DNA replication

One of the secrets of the success of living organisms on Earth is the ease with which DNA can be replicated – faithfully copied to be passed on to new cells. The process is simple, but ingenious.

DNA REPLICATION

DNA forms the basis of all life on Earth – every organism uses DNA as its genetic material and depends on it to ensure the survival of its genes in the next generation. What underlies this extraordinary ubiquity is the ease with which DNA can be faithfully replicated. DNA is easy to copy because of the complementary nature of its base pairs. Each strand of the double helix can be used as the template for a new facing strand. Essentially, the double helix unwinds, and the separate facing strands of DNA 'pick up' free bases to complement the existing ones, effectively producing two new strands.

Stages in DNA replication

1 *DNA unzips: Enzymes separate the two strands of bases, rather like unzipping a zip.*

MISTAKES AND MUTATIONS

Mistakes in DNA replication could be serious. Change just one base and you would change a codon, which in turn would cause the wrong amino acid to be inserted during translation (pages 20–21). Such a change is called a mutation. Sometimes this does not affect the resulting protein too much, and sometimes it's positively beneficial, but if the amino acid substitution happens in a crucial zone of the protein it may fail to fold up properly and won't function correctly. Even worse is a mutation that transforms a codon into a 'stop' codon, preventing the protein from being made at all. Changes to a single base pair (known as single point mutations) are responsible for such devastating diseases as sickle cell anaemia, and can also cause a cell to become cancerous.

Mutations happen in a number of ways. The DNA replication enzymes can make mistakes. UV rays, radiation, toxic chemicals and highly reactive by-products of normal cell metabolism, known as free radicals, can damage DNA. Such damage is fixed by repair enzymes, which replace the affected bases, but these too can make mistakes. Viruses can also cause mutations. In fact your DNA is constantly being mutated but your cells are equipped with efficient DNA-checking enzymes, which spot mistakes and repair them. Thanks to these quality control enzymes, mistakes are made only about once every ten billion bases, instead of once every few thousand. It's the difference between life and death.

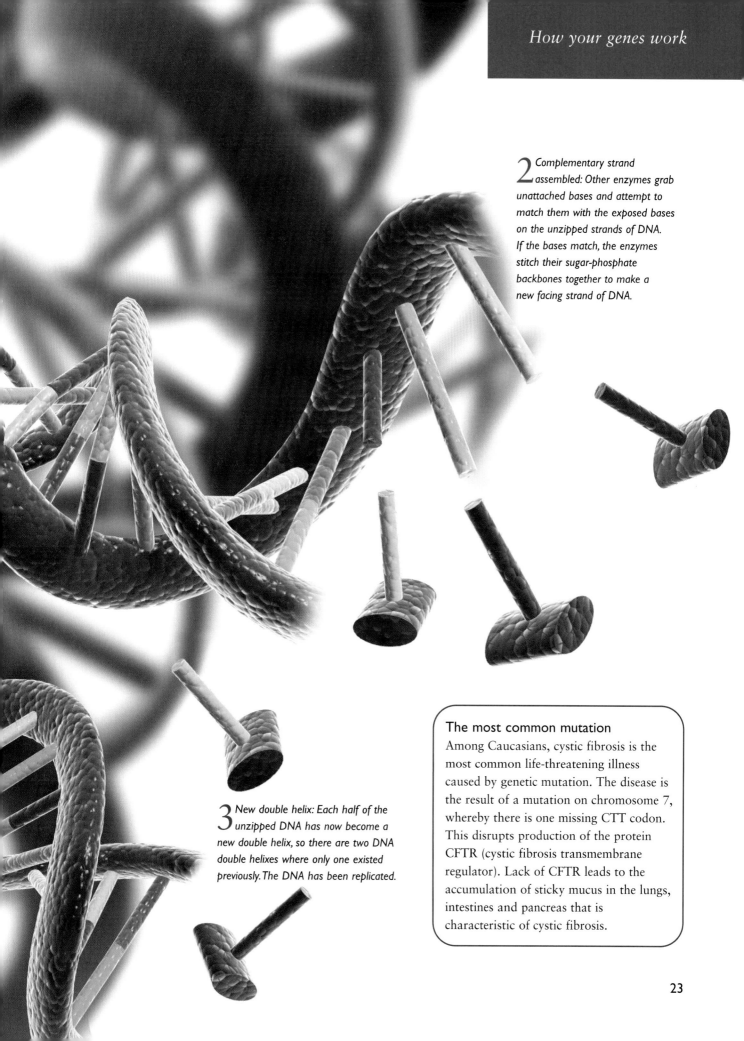

2 *Complementary strand assembled: Other enzymes grab unattached bases and attempt to match them with the exposed bases on the unzipped strands of DNA. If the bases match, the enzymes stitch their sugar-phosphate backbones together to make a new facing strand of DNA.*

3 *New double helix: Each half of the unzipped DNA has now become a new double helix, so there are two DNA double helixes where only one existed previously. The DNA has been replicated.*

The most common mutation

Among Caucasians, cystic fibrosis is the most common life-threatening illness caused by genetic mutation. The disease is the result of a mutation on chromosome 7, whereby there is one missing CTT codon. This disrupts production of the protein CFTR (cystic fibrosis transmembrane regulator). Lack of CFTR leads to the accumulation of sticky mucus in the lungs, intestines and pancreas that is characteristic of cystic fibrosis.

23

Cell division

You are literally not the same person you were two years ago — almost every cell in your body has died and been replaced with new ones. The process that makes this possible is responsible for both evolution and cancer.

As you develop from a single fertilised cell into a complete human being your DNA is replicated a million billion times.

From the trillions of cells in the body, each with its own structure and functions, scientists have established that there are about 200 basic cell types, all containing a nucleus which houses genetic material and other structures called organelles, which fulfill specific functions. Cells combine to form tissues and there are four major tissue types:

- **Epithelial tissue** covers exposed parts of the body, forming a barrier. Epithelial cells line the digestive, respiratory and urinary tract, for example. These cells also produce glandular secretions.

- **Muscle tissue** contracts, enabling your body to move both voluntarily and involuntarily, pushing foodstuffs through the digestive system, for example. The heart is muscle tissue.
- **Neural tissue** carries information and conducts electrical impulses. It is involved in sensing and initiating an appropriate response to change in the environment.
- **Connective tissue** provides structural support for other tissues and organs, and stores energy. It forms the skin and the skeleton.

MITOSIS

Many cell types need continuous replacement by cell division, both during periods of growth and to compensate for cell damage. In most cells, this necessitates the production of two identical daughter cells containing a full complement of chromosomes, in a process known as mitosis. DNA replication happens when cells are about to divide.

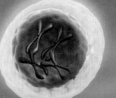

1 **The DNA in the nucleus** bunches up into 46 chromosomes, and these are duplicated to give X-shaped double chromosomes.

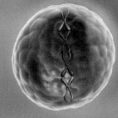

2 **Thread-like structures** called spindles stretch across the cell and the double chromosomes arrange themselves on the spindle.

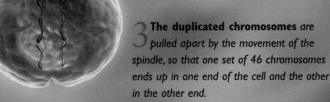

3 **The duplicated chromosomes** are pulled apart by the movement of the spindle, so that one set of 46 chromosomes ends up in one end of the cell and the other in the other end.

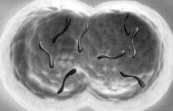

4 **The cell splits in two** so that there are now two 'daughter' cells, each with a full complement of identical chromosomes.

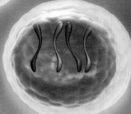

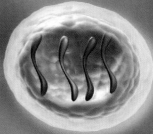

MEIOSIS

Every cell in your body is made by mitosis, with the exception of your gametes
– your sperm or egg cells. These undergo a slightly different process called
meiosis, where four daughter cells are made rather than just two, and each one
ends up with only half a set of chromosomes.

1 The chromosomes are replicated *to give double chromosomes, in the same way as in mitosis.*

2 During a process *called crossing over, matching chromosome pairs make contact and intertwine. Sections of chromosome are swapped between matching chromosome arms such that genes are 'shuffled' between the matching chromosome pairs.*

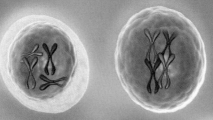

3 Spindles form *and half of the chromosome pairs are pulled into each side of the cell.*

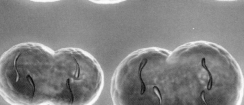

4 The cell divides, *to give two cells each with a set of 23 double chromosomes (instead of 46 single chromosomes, as in mitosis).*

More spindles *form and now the double chromosomes are pulled apart into single chromosomes, as in stage 3 of mitosis.*

6 The cells divide *one last time to give four daughter cells, each with 23 chromosomes. These chromosomes are different from the chromosomes in every other cell of your body because of crossing over.*

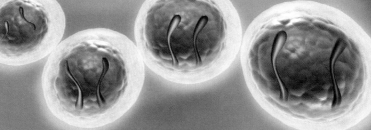

EVOLUTION

Evolution depends on variety. Only if the members of a
species vary slightly can natural selection pick those best
adapted to their environment for success. Meiosis and
sexual reproduction provide one source of this variety.
In sexual reproduction genes from both parents come
together to form a new individual, while the genetic
mixture is further shaken up by the crossing over that
takes place during the formation of gametes (step 2 in
meiosis, above). Ultimately, however, the main source of
variation is mutation. Random mutations are happening
all the time to the genome of every organism. Most of
these mutations either have no effect or damage the
organism's chances of survival, but a few are beneficial
and make the bearers more likely to survive, breed and
pass on their mutation. In this way new species arise and
become better adapted to their environments.

How genes are passed on

What does it mean when someone says you've got your father's nose or your mother's eyes? How are traits passed on, and why do you get some but not others? If your parents both have brown eyes, how can you have blue eyes?

GENOTYPES AND PHENOTYPES

There is a huge gulf between the mathematical logic of a DNA sequence and the familiar features that make up an individual human being. How does DNA pass on, for example, a double-jointed thumb, a receding hairline or blue eyes? And why are specific traits passed to some but not all offspring? In practice, the pathway that leads from the DNA sequence that makes up a gene (the genotype) to the physical expression of that gene as a characteristic or trait (the phenotype), is uncertain: few such pathways have been worked out. However, to understand the principle of inheritance, it is important to grasp that there is a difference between genotype and phenotype.

CHROMOSOMES AND ALLELES

Everyone has two copies of every gene. Genes are located on chromosomes, and there are 23 pairs of chromosomes (46 in all). One of each pair comes from the mother and one from the father, so an individual's genome is made up of half of their mother's genes and half of their father's.

The two copies of each gene are called alleles, and not surprisingly as they come from different sources, they are not identical. For many traits one allele is dominant over the other; the non-dominant allele is said to be recessive. Eye colour, for example, is largely determined by one gene which codes for either brown or blue eyes. The allele for brown eyes is always dominant (B) over an allele for blue eyes, which is recessive (b). If an individual inherits a brown-eye gene from their mother and a blue-eye gene from their father, the dominant brown gene determines the individual's eye colour as brown, even though their genotype is a combination of brown and blue. Two blue-eyed parents will always produce blue-eyed children, since they cannot carry a brown eye allele and have blue eyes.

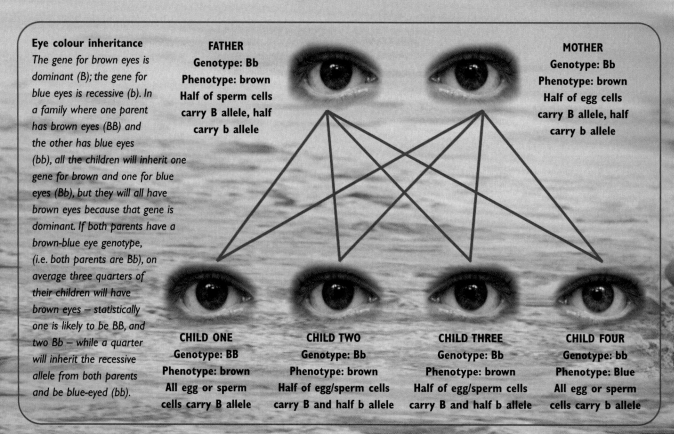

Eye colour inheritance
The gene for brown eyes is dominant (B); the gene for blue eyes is recessive (b). In a family where one parent has brown eyes (BB) and the other has blue eyes (bb), all the children will inherit one gene for brown and one for blue eyes (Bb), but they will all have brown eyes because that gene is dominant. If both parents have a brown-blue eye genotype, (i.e. both parents are Bb), on average three quarters of their children will have brown eyes – statistically one is likely to be BB, and two Bb – while a quarter will inherit the recessive allele from both parents and be blue-eyed (bb).

FATHER
Genotype: Bb
Phenotype: brown
Half of sperm cells carry B allele, half carry b allele

MOTHER
Genotype: Bb
Phenotype: brown
Half of egg cells carry B allele, half carry b allele

CHILD ONE
Genotype: BB
Phenotype: brown
All egg or sperm cells carry B allele

CHILD TWO
Genotype: Bb
Phenotype: brown
Half of egg/sperm cells carry B and half b allele

CHILD THREE
Genotype: Bb
Phenotype: brown
Half of egg/sperm cells carry B and half b allele

CHILD FOUR
Genotype: bb
Phenotype: Blue
All egg or sperm cells carry b allele

Family resemblances are among over 13,000 genetically inherited human traits that have been identified by researchers. Over 5000 of these traits are diseases or abnormalities.

Hereditary traits

A few traits conform to a simple pattern of inheritance. Examples include dimples and the ability to wiggle your ears. However, most hereditary traits are polygenic, that is, they are influenced by more than one gene. Even in a trait like eye colour which is largely determined by one gene, the influence of other genes affects the amount and location of eye pigments, which is why eye colours other than blue or brown exist, such as green, grey and hazel. Hair colour is another polygenic trait. Sometimes the expression of a gene will skip a generation, so, for example, a girl with red-hair and blue eyes could have parents who both have brown hair and brown eyes, but have inherited her own colouring from a grandparent.

Eyes of different colours

About 1 per cent of the population have eyes of different colours, including rock legend David Bowie. This can result from childhood trauma: a blow to the eye — from a ball, perhaps, or a punch — can make the iris darken by increasing the amount of the pigment melanin. However, the phenomenon can also result from what scientists call genetic mosaicism. During early embryonic development the eye colour gene in one cell mutates. If this cell — and all the cells that arise from it by replication — develops into one eye, while the other eye develops from a cell without the mutation, the eyes can end up different colours.

Genes and ageing

Slowing down or reversing the ageing process has long been the dream of scientists and physicians. Now, with the discovery of genes that may influence or cause ageing, that dream may be coming closer to reality.

COMING APART AT THE SEAMS

A crucial clue to the source of ageing at a cellular level came with the discovery of the Hayflick limit, so-called after its discoverer, Leonard Hayflick. The Hayflick limit is the maximum number of times that a cell grown in a laboratory culture will divide before stopping and dying. The number varies between species, and corresponds to the average lifespan of each species. The Hayflick limit for mouse cells is about 15, and mice live for around three years. For the cells of the Galapagos giant tortoise, which lives up to 175 years, the limit is 110. The Hayflick limit for humans is between 50 and 70.

Telomeres and telomerase

The existence of such a limit suggested that something in the cell was wearing down as it divided. That something has been found to be the telomeres, the 'caps' at the end of each chromosome that stop the DNA from unravelling like a loose thread at the edge of a garment. Every time a cell divides, its telomeres get a little shorter until finally they can no longer do their job and the chromosome starts to come apart. The cell can no longer divide, and instead becomes old and dies. This process, repeated all over the body, is partly responsible for ageing.

Some cells make an enzyme called telomerase, which can rebuild telomeres and protect chromosomes. Cells that make this enzyme include blood and skin stem cells, sperm and eggs, and these are believed to be effectively immortal. Most other cells stop making telomerase soon after they come into existence. If something goes wrong and they start making it again, they become cancerous.

UNDER FIRE

A lot of ageing is caused by build-up of damage to DNA and other cell components. Most of this damage is done by free radicals, highly reactive molecules that are produced internally as a by-product of normal metabolism, and also impact from outside in the form of UV light, radiation, toxic chemicals, viruses and so on. Free radicals career about the cell damaging anything that gets in their way, mutating the DNA and making

other molecules sticky so that the cell clogs up. When a cell accumulates too much damage it can no longer be repaired and dies – or worse, it becomes cancerous because it has acquired too many mutations.

Antioxidant *attacking and neutralising a free radical. This is a vital part of the protection mechanism for the body's cells.*

A gene *being transcribed and translated to make a protective enzyme that 'mops up' free radicals.*

Telomere unwinding *– after a given number of cell divisions, telomeres can no longer protect the end of the cell's chromosomes and the chromosomes start to unravel. Cell division is not possible without the chromosomes, so the cell ages and dies.*

Free radicals *caused by radiation attack the cell from the outside.*

Glucose molecules, *the result of free radical attack, stick to proteins and clog up the cell.*

The cell membrane *becomes leaky under fire from free radicals, damaging the integrity of the cell.*

Mitochondria *are the powerhouses of the cell, burning oxygen to produce energy, but free radicals are a by-product of this process.*

A free radical *molecule emerges from a mitochondria.*

THE METHUSELAH EFFECT

Telomere damage is just one cause of ageing. Experiments have shown that it is possible to extend the lifespan of animals by altering key genes that are involved in ageing. Examples of these key genes include the klotho, methuselah and daf-2 genes, discovered in mice, fruit flies and nematode worms respectively. These genes probably have counterparts in the human genome. Experiments on human fibroblasts (cells that help to make and maintain skin) found 61 genes associated with ageing. These were involved in a variety of processes, including cell division, collagen manufacture and the inflammatory response.

Mop up genes

Many genes that help to slow or prevent ageing are probably involved in the system that defends us against free radicals, by making, protecting or enhancing the action of antioxidants. These are agents that mop up free radicals before they can do too much damage. Other anti-ageing genes help to repair free radical damage after it has happened.

Can we live longer?

Doing something about ageing by tinkering with genes is going to be far more difficult than simply identifying the genes involved. Scientists must determine exactly how the genes work, if they have any other functions, how they interact and what the consequences might be if the genes were altered. Changes made in pursuit of anti-ageing might turn out, for example, to increase the risk of cancer and be counter-productive.

Fetal development

Possibly the genome's most amazing feat is transforming a single cell — the fertilised egg — into a complex working organism composed of trillions of cells each in their appointed place and performing their allotted tasks.

THE COMPASS OF DEVELOPMENT

Hox genes (see below) and the genes they control code for products that tell the cells in a developing embryo where they are. This is the crucial information that cells need in order to know what to turn into. Once a cell knows that it is in the 'heart' location, the appropriate genes can be activated and it can set off down the path towards becoming cardiac muscle. As it divides it can issue further instructions to its daughter cells and the cells around them, marshalling them like a foreman leading a gang of builders. But first the cell needs to know where it is, and this is where the developmental genes come in: they code for chemicals called morphogens.

Morphogens – setting the poles

Changing concentrations of morphogens in the embryo (called concentration gradients), and in particular the interaction between concentration gradients for different kinds of morphogen, are what enable a cell to locate itself in the body of the embryo. Morphogens come into play from the very beginning of development, because the egg cell itself contains a concentration gradient of morphogens. These give the egg cell a 'head' and a 'tail' – or a top and bottom, or a north and south pole, if you prefer. So before cell division even starts, the newly fertilised egg has an orientation thanks to its morphogens, and this forms the basis for all later development.

When the fertilised egg divides for the first time, the daughter cell formed from the 'head' end of the egg has lots of morphogens, while the daughter cell at the 'tail' end does not. Cued by their relative amounts of morphogen, each daughter cell then activates the relevant genes. In the 'head' cell, these are genes that set in train the developmental pathways for the formation of the head, thorax and arms; in the 'tail' cell, they are genes for the abdomen and legs.

HOX GENES

Geneticists investigating the development of the fruit fly discovered a set of genes that controlled the insect's body plan, determining which part became a leg, which an eye, which the thorax, and so on. All of these genes had in common an initial sequence of bases that was called a 'homeobox', and the genes were called Hox genes in a shortened version of this.

The scientists found that swapping Hox genes around could make things grow in the wrong places – a leg where an antenna should be, for example, or an extra mouth in place of an eye. But the real surprise came when geneticists looked for similar genes elsewhere in the animal kingdom, and found them

everywhere, including in the human genome. So similar are human Hox genes to fruit fly ones that a human gene inserted into a fruit fly genome will not impair the normal development of a healthy fly.

There are 39 human Hox genes, on four different chromosomes. The four sets are arranged along their chromosomes in a linear fashion corresponding to the layout of the human body, so that the ones for the head are followed by the ones for the thorax and arms, then those for the abdomen and legs.

Hox genes work by controlling other genes. They all include the code for a region of a protein shaped like a screw, which is able to 'screw' onto DNA turning other genes on and off. The timing of Hox gene activation in turn determines the activation of other genes that coordinate development.

There are 289 known genes for human diseases, of which 177 have direct counterparts in the fruit fly.

Budding limbs – 28-day-old fetus

The development of limbs from the central trunk of an embryo is triggered by a gene called distal-less. A closely related gene controls limb development in fruit flies and lobsters. Once a limb bud starts to grow, the developmental pathways of the cells in the bud are determined by their position. For instance, in an arm bud, the cells at the tip of the bud will grow into the hand and fingers, while the cells on the top side of the bud will become the top side of the arm.

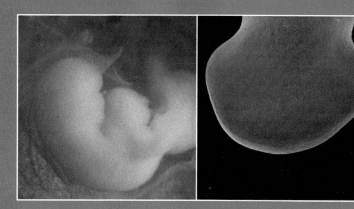

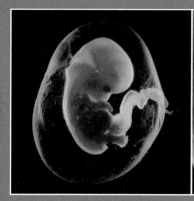
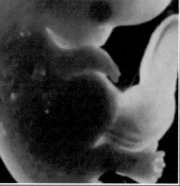

Eight weeks old

During the first few weeks of pregnancy organ and limb differentiation greatly outstrips fetal growth. This eight-week old fetus is still just 4cm long and weighs less than 10g, but all the major organs are in place and the arms and legs have moved on from indistinct buds to proto-limbs.

Four months old

By the fourth month of pregnancy, the baby's arm has a recognisable wrist, forearm, hand and fingers. The upper limbs are more fully developed than the lower limbs at this stage.

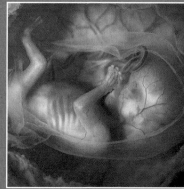
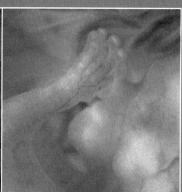

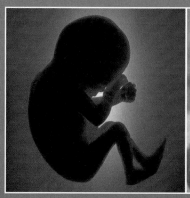

Five months old

By the end of the fifth month of development, the baby's hands have well differentiated fingers. An increase in muscular coordination, as well as the maturing nervous system, now make it possible for babies to start sucking their thumb.

Infancy and childhood

The work of your genes is just beginning at birth, as your genetic heritage extends into every corner of your life. In childhood, genes influence your health, physical development, personality, intelligence and even your likes and dislikes.

One B lymphocyte cell can make 10 million antibodies per hour.

THE PARENTAL LEGACY

A child's genome is made up of matching sets of genes – one set from each parent. Some of these genes follow the pattern of dominance/recessiveness discussed on pages 26–27, so that the child will resemble one parent or the other in the trait coded for by those genes. But many traits, including height, weight and facial features, are determined by a number of genes, so that children inherit a blend of their parents' characteristics.

Skipping a generation

Some traits run in families but don't show up in every generation. This happens when the trait is coded for by a recessive allele. Several generations of a family may carry the allele in their genomes and pass it on to their children, but it will show up only when it lands next to a corresponding allele that isn't dominant.

BUILDING UP IMMUNITY

Heredity is responsible for a range of illnesses that afflict children, from such devastating genetic disorders as Tay-Sachs or progeria, to chronic problems such as asthma and hay fever. But a child's genetic inheritance also forms the basis of his or her developing immune system.

A newborn baby is vulnerable to a range of infections because part of the immune system is immature. Babies are born with innate immunity – the generic part of the system that attacks foreign organisms (pathogens) without any degree of specificity – but have to build up acquired immunity. This is the part of the immune system that is able to learn to recognise pathogens so that a more precise, faster and more powerful response can be mounted.

The key component of acquired immunity is the antibody, a protein that is specialised to recognise markers on individual pathogens, stick to them and alert the rest of the immune system. The antibody is specific – it is able to perfectly match the shape of pathogens, even ones the immune system has never encountered before. Antibodies can take hundreds of millions of different forms, but they are coded for by genes, and there isn't space in the human genome for even a fraction of this number of genes.

The hundreds of millions of different possible antibodies are generated by just a few hundred genes arranged into a system called the 'generator of diversity' (GOD). The genes code for regions of antibodies, and the GOD works by mixing and matching them to create different outcomes.

Hypermutation – creating antibodies

Hundreds of thousands of antibodies circulate round the body. When one encounters a pathogen that is a close structural match it swings into action. A cell called a lymphocyte makes more copies of the antibody, but the copies all vary slightly, the result of somatic hypermutation, where the antibody genes mutate a million times faster than normal. Whichever new variant is a closer match for the pathogen is then used as the template for further hypermutation, until a perfectly matching antibody is created.

NATURE VS NURTURE

Each child has an individual genetically programmed timetable of physical and mental development. However, adverse environmental factors can disrupt the process. Children are biologically predisposed to develop language skills, for example, but if the environment is not sufficiently stimulating, these skills will develop late. Conversely, a genetically 'average' child, raised in a stimulating environment, may outstrip a child with a more favourable genetic inheritance. Early or late walking seems to make no difference to later skill in balance and co-ordination. Generally, the children in a family tend to walk and talk at roughly the same ages, suggesting a genetic link.

The greatest influence?
Genetics influences temperament, and a parent's temperament will influence a child's and vice versa. Those who study child development, however, believe that the influence of a child's peers on such factors as speech and action is at least as important as that of parents.

Looking for clues
Parents are usually the first people to spot that a child may have developmental delay, that is, be reaching milestones later than their peers. This may be due to a chromosomal problem or a complication of pregnancy. Early intervention can significantly improve a child's intellectual, behavioural and social skills.

Peer pressure
A recent, small-scale study in California, noted that early attendance at nursery school, and therefore exposure to other children and their infections, reduced the risk of childhood leukaemia, presumably by boosting the children's immune system early.

Puberty

Puberty is a stage of profound development. The transformation is controlled by the interaction of genes and hormones, which combine to produce wide-ranging physical and psychological changes.

The hypothalamus has a richer blood supply than any other part of the body.

LOSING INHIBITIONS

Fetal and infant development are dramatic, after which the human body calms down. Although there are changes during childhood, these are more in terms of growth than development. Puberty marks a second phase of dramatic developmental transformation, which has been likened to the metamorphosis of insects and amphibians.

The age at which puberty starts depends on four main factors:

- **Genetics** Girls tend to mature around the age their mothers did (and boys may follow their fathers), although studies of identical twins show that they do not necessarily reach puberty together.
- **Nutrition** Girls, in particular, need to be a certain weight, with sufficient body fat to sustain a possible pregnancy, in order for puberty to begin.
- **Environment** For example, stress can delay the onset of puberty.
- **Hormones** These chemical messengers are proteins made in response to a genetic instruction.

To understand what triggers puberty, it helps to understand why it doesn't happen earlier.

From hormone to hormone

The agents of pubertal change are the sex hormones testosterone and oestrogen. In large enough amounts these cause the maturation of the gonads – the testes and ovaries – and the development of secondary sexual characteristics. But these hormones are made by the gonads themselves – the amounts produced depend on the levels of other hormones called gonadotropins made by the pituitary gland. Gonadotropin levels in turn depend on the levels of the hormone gonadotropin-releasing factor (GnRF), made by the hypothalamus.

During childhood, sex hormone levels are kept low by means of a negative feedback system between the hypothalamus and the pituitary gland (see right). As a result, the gonads are not stimulated to make sex hormones and mature.

The puberty trigger
Prior to puberty, hormonal activity is held in check through negative feedback from the hypothalamus to the pituitary gland. The sensitivity of the hypothalamus to sex hormones inhibits the pituitary gland and consequent activity. At puberty this sensitivity is lost, setting up a chain of hormonal activity and triggering the changes of puberty.

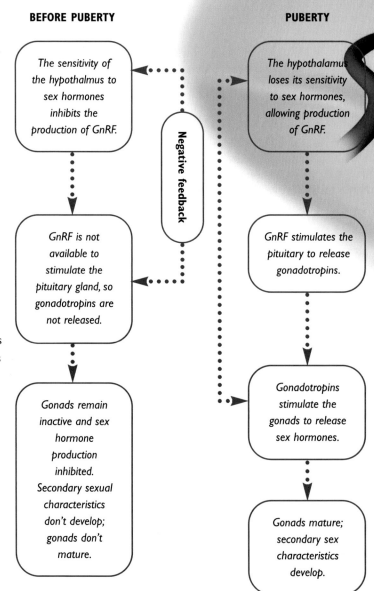

BEFORE PUBERTY

The sensitivity of the hypothalmus to sex hormones inhibits the production of GnRF.

GnRF is not available to stimulate the pituitary gland, so gonadotropins are not released.

Gonads remain inactive and sex hormone production inhibited. Secondary sexual characteristics don't develop; gonads don't mature.

Negative feedback

PUBERTY

The hypothalamus loses its sensitivity to sex hormones, allowing production of GnRF.

GnRF stimulates the pituitary to release gonadotropins.

Gonadotropins stimulate the gonads to release sex hormones.

Gonads mature; secondary sex characteristics develop.

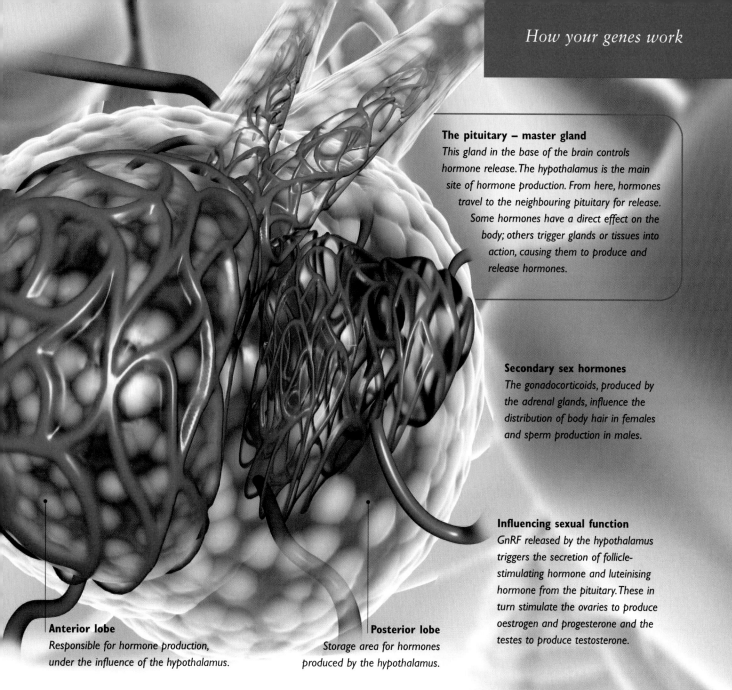

The pituitary – master gland
This gland in the base of the brain controls hormone release. The hypothalamus is the main site of hormone production. From here, hormones travel to the neighbouring pituitary for release. Some hormones have a direct effect on the body; others trigger glands or tissues into action, causing them to produce and release hormones.

Secondary sex hormones
The gonadocorticoids, produced by the adrenal glands, influence the distribution of body hair in females and sperm production in males.

Influencing sexual function
GnRF released by the hypothalamus triggers the secretion of follicle-stimulating hormone and luteinising hormone from the pituitary. These in turn stimulate the ovaries to produce oestrogen and progesterone and the testes to produce testosterone.

Anterior lobe
Responsible for hormone production, under the influence of the hypothalamus.

Posterior lobe
Storage area for hormones produced by the hypothalamus.

Puberty begins when the hypothalamus starts to lose its sensitivity to sex hormones. It is not known for certain why this happens, but it may be because of the way that the genes that make sex hormone receptors are expressed. As a result GnRF levels rise. The pituitary responds by making more gonadotropins, which prod the gonads into action. They start to mature, making more sex hormones, which increase the rate of maturation and start to affect the rest of the body.

PRIMARY AND SECONDARY CHANGES
The primary sexual characteristics are the gonads and genitals – the testes and penis in men, and the ovaries, uterus and vagina in women. Secondary sexual characteristics include the growth of breasts, pubic hair, menstruation, wet dreams and different body size and composition. At the beginning of puberty, boys and girls have similar proportions of body fat, muscle mass and skeletal mass. After puberty, women have developed twice as much body fat as men, whereas men have one and a half times the skeletal and muscle mass of women.

Maturation of the reproductive organs and other pubertal changes cause boys and girls to become fertile. In girls the first menstruation, the menarche, represents the integration of new hormonal cycles. Boys become fertile when meiosis begins in the germ cells of the testes and the spermatic ducts hollow out to form a channel for the sperm to pass from the testes into the urethra.

Adulthood

As you grow older your genes continue to exert control not just over your body, but also over your life. Your choice of mate, leisure pursuits and mental health are all influenced more or less by genetics.

IDENTICALS ATTRACT

There are lots of theories about why people fall for each other, but some research findings have suggested that genetics plays a large part in choosing a mate. Comparisons of partners show that they resemble each other in all sorts of subtle ways, such as the relative lengths of certain finger joints or the levels of dissolved gases in the blood. What's bringing partners together is a subconscious drive to pair up people with similar genes.

The selfish gene

At first glance this doesn't seem to make evolutionary sense – inbreeding results in a higher proportion of congenital defects, and the more mixing of the gene pool the healthier the species. But consider it on the level of individual genes. The most successful genes are those that ensure they get passed on to the next generation, and what better way to do this than mate with someone carrying similar genes? The chances of that gene being passed on to an offspring are doubled.

The greatest taboo

Normally the social programming of the incest taboo prevents us from being interested in those whose genomes are closest to our own – our family. But some scientists believe that the countervailing urge to match your genes with similar ones is responsible for the phenomenon of long-lost siblings falling in love at first sight when they meet. Having not developed an incest taboo, they bear the full brunt of the urge to mate like with like.

THE NEED FOR VARIETY – MHC PROTEINS

There is one area of the genome where scientists have found that opposites do attract – the genes for a class of proteins called major histocompatibility complex (MHC) proteins. These help the immune system to tell friend from foe, but are also used by invading pathogens as anchoring sites via which they can gain entry and infect the cell. A population with variable MHC proteins is more resistant to diseases, because the disease-causing pathogens are specialised for different MHC targets.

Researchers have found that the more different two people's MHC genes are, the more likely they are to be attracted to one another. By bringing together widely differing MHC genes, parents can ensure that their offspring will have new and unusual MHC proteins, making them more resistant to disease.

It's not yet clear, however, how partners sense this sort of obscure genetic information about each other. It could be that the information is carried by pheromones – hormone-like scents that everyone gives off and which can produce powerful subconscious reactions in others.

MATTER INFLUENCING MIND

Several projects have linked psychological disorders – including schizophrenia, depression and alcoholism – to specific genes. This doesn't mean that they are controlled by a single gene, or that having that gene dooms an individual to a disorder, but it suggests that genetics may be as important as life events and psychology in causing such illnesses. A gene for anxiety has been located, and a gene that codes for receptors for dopamine, a chemical messenger in the brain, has been linked to 'novelty seeking'. According to one theory, people with this gene make fewer dopamine receptors, and therefore need more emotional and physiological arousal to raise brain activity levels above a certain 'boredom threshold'. To get the arousal they seek exciting, even dangerous, experiences.

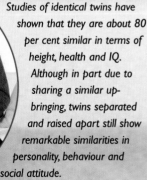

Similar but different
Studies of identical twins have shown that they are about 80 per cent similar in terms of height, health and IQ. Although in part due to sharing a similar up-bringing, twins separated and raised apart still show remarkable similarities in personality, behaviour and social attitude.

Choosing a partner

Genes have a strong influence on who we select as a mate. Studies of Hutterite couples – a North American religious community whose 35,000 members can trace their ancestry to a group of just 80 European immigrants – found that only 10 per cent matched for certain kinds of MHC proteins. This suggests that genes in this area of DNA have an influence on mate selection in humans (it had previously been shown in mice). Further studies showed that miscarriage rates were highest among couples whose MHC were more closely matched.

Old age – signs of ageing

Everyone's body gradually wears out, but the rate at which this takes place is partly determined by genetics. Genes play a significant part in determining whether and when Alzheimer's disease or cancer will develop.

Ever-decreasing circles
As individual cells wear out, die and are no longer replaced, and as the processes that they carried out are steadily eroded, the tissues and organs of the body bear the impact.

THE SANDS OF TIME

The steady accumulation of free radical damage, the inexorable unwinding of the telomeres, the gradual gumming up of cellular machinery and the inevitable build-up of mutations and mistakes in the DNA makes senescence unavoidable for all but a select few of the body's cells. The stem cells of the bone marrow that generate new blood cells are among these lucky immortals, but they decrease in number with the years and can scarcely hold back the tide of time as it washes over the rest of the body.

The mind, however, is a different matter. As life expectancy in the developed world has increased, so more and more people are living into old age and falling prey to diseases that were once rarely seen. The greatest of these threats to geriatric health is Alzheimer's disease. At one time it was thought that senile dementia was a natural consequence of ageing, but it is now known that Alzheimer's is indeed a disease. Nonetheless, many elderly people who stay healthy can expect to retain sharpness of intellect right up until the end.

People who have fewer children tend to live longer – more of their energy goes into self repair.

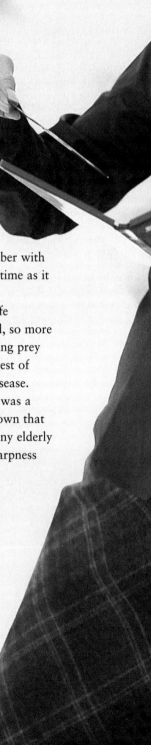

The skin
As the skin loses elasticity and moisture it becomes thin, dry and sagging.

The lungs
These struggle to clear away fluid that impedes oxygen absorption.

The heart and circulation
Deposits of scaly plaque build up on the walls of the arteries while the elasticity that normally allows them to help the heart with its pumping is gradually lost. The valves of the heart become weak and leaky. These changes to the circulatory system mean that less blood reaches the heart and the rest of the body, so that all of the tissues become progressively less well equipped to stave off ageing. In this way, many of the processes of ageing are like vicious circles.

Liver and kidneys
These organs become less efficient at neutralising and removing toxins, so that they increasingly build up and cause yet more damage.

Digestive system
The system becomes less efficient at extracting health-sustaining nourishment from food.

Bones and joints
The bones become brittle and joints ossified and stiff, while the muscles become smaller and weaker.

GENETIC THREATS TO HEALTH IN OLD AGE

Genetic time bombs *Lurking in the genome of a few individuals out of every thousand are disease genes that aren't expressed until adulthood. Among them are the genes for crippling disorders such as Huntington's disease, late-onset ataxia and motor neurone disease. For reasons not properly understood these genes, or their products, are not activated until later in life.*

Cancer *Cells normally limit their own division but if the genes controlling this process become faulty, or if genes that were active in earlier stages of life become reactivated, the cell can start to multiply uncontrollably and become cancerous. Genes involved in this process are called oncogenes. One of these, a mutated version of a gene called p53, which normally reins in cell growth, is present in about half of all human tumours, but up to 20 oncogenes have to become active before a cell becomes cancerous.*

Alzheimer's disease *In normal ageing gradual loss of neurons means that memory is impeded and some mental processes slow down, but the number of neurons lost is so small compared to the overall number that this effect is relatively insignificant. A large number of people, however, carry a gene that increases their chances of developing the neural plaques that cause Alzheimer's. This gene, ApoE, belongs to a family that code for apolipoproteins, molecules that store and transport cholesterol around the body. ApoE comes in three alleles – E2, E3 and E4. E2 and E3 are healthy versions, but E4 is linked to Alzheimer's. The difference between this version of the gene and the others is just one base out of 900.*

There is some evidence to suggest that reducing calorie intake throughout life may extend lifespan.

2

Staying healthy
for life

A LIFETIME OF GOOD HEALTH

Every person is the product of their genes, passed on from their parents. How or if these genes are expressed, however, will vary between family members, so siblings can look, behave and develop very differently. Health status is only partly genetic: many things, from a person's height to their risk of cancer, are also influenced by their environment and lifestyle.

 43 *Taking a look at other family members can be a good, but not infallible, indicator of how an individual will grow and mature.*

 46 *Recording a family health history can help you to assess whether you might be susceptible to a genetic, or other health, problem.*

 49 *The environment can have a huge impact on health and well-being through life, and starts to affect us even before we are born.*

Knowing what's normal

Tracing a family's medical geneaology can highlight patterns of inheritance for syndromes and diseases. This can be useful for allaying fears or to alert individuals to inherited tendencies so they can reduce their risk of ill-health.

WHAT IS YOUR GENETIC INHERITANCE?

Half of all our genes come from each parent via the chromosomes carried in the gametes (the eggs and sperm). On average, one-quarter comes from each of our grandparents, but this is only an average because in reality the chromosomes are randomly distributed in our parents' gametes. So, for example, depending on the individual egg that we come from, we may have received more of our maternal grandmother's genes, whereas a brother or sister may have received more of our maternal grandfather's genes. In other words, we get half our genetic material from each parent, but in each half we get varying amounts of the genetic material that they received from their parents. This is why it is often possible to pick out in a child a physical similarity to a particular grandparent or more distant relative, and also why some siblings look so very different from each other.

Knowing your own family tree can give clues to your genetic inheritance, but there are about 32,000 genes that go to make up each of us and only a proportion of these determine looks or development. Looks are not a predictor of health problems – just because you look like your Great

Striking similarities
A child may resemble one parent more than the other, but this does not mean they have more of that parent's genes: everyone inherits genes equally from their mother and father.

Aunt Mary, for example, this does not mean you will have the same health as she did, good or bad. This is because we are also a product of the way our genes interact with our environment.

DEFINING SYNDROMES

A syndrome is a number of abnormalities, which can be mild or severe, but which always occur together. Often the abnormalities can be traced to a single event that may have occurred in development – for example, an interruption to the blood supply during a crucial fetal growth period. Or it may be because a single gene that controls an aspect of development does not function properly. If the cause is a mutation in a gene that stops the gene from working correctly, the same range of abnormalities, or syndrome, may be passed on in the family. This would be a genetic syndrome.

There are literally thousands of genetic syndromes. Most are benign, such as fragile fingernails and hair, but some have potentially severe health consequences.

TWIN STUDIES

Twin studies are in the forefront of the scientific attempt to disentangle genetic causes (nature) from environmental causes (nurture) for a particular characteristic. Comparing concordance rates – the degree of sameness – for a particular characteristic in identical (monozygotic) and non-identical (dizygotic) twins has been used as a way to measure the genetic component of that trait.

For example, with a truly genetic disorder, such as Huntington's disease, if one identical twin has the gene for the disease, then the other identical twin will also have the gene. Both of them will be expected to develop the disease at some point in their lives. Conversely, if one identical twin does not have the gene, neither will the other. (For this reason, identical twins considering having genetic testing are usually encouraged to discuss the testing with their twin: if there is disagreement the 'right to know' outweighs the 'right to remain ignorant'.) In contrast, in non-identical twins, the same gene will be inherited by both twins only 50 per cent of the time, and 50 per cent of the time they will have inherited a different gene from their parent. This means that one twin could develop the disease and not the other.

The influence of environment

Other traits are less clear-cut and the genetic inheritance is influenced, to a greater or lesser extent, by environment. For example, height is known to be about 90 per cent heritable and genetics accounts for most of the variation in height that we see in the population, but environmental factors such as diet can also play a role. In contrast, the likelihood of having a traffic accident is not linked to a heritable trait.

Genetics plays a role in causing schizophrenia, but it is not the entire cause – environmental factors also play a part. The search for the environmental factors responsible has covered influenza (or another obstetrical factor) during the second trimester of pregnancy, a low birth weight, and disordered development. However, each of these is predicted to have only a very small effect, and in most cases where these factors are involved the individuals concerned do not go on to develop schizophrenia. (The background population risk of schizophrenia is about one per cent.)

Studies of twins have provided us with estimates of how much genetics and environment contribute to a wide variety of characteristics and diseases, such as hypertension, intelligence, mental illness, behavioural factors and diabetes. Another useful twist on this method of assessing the environmental component in a particular trait is to look at identical twins who have grown up apart.

DETERMINING WHAT IS NORMAL

Just as we know, for example, that our nose or hands or build are like a particular relative's, so we know – simply by looking around at our own family and other families

Knowing me, knowing you
For a trait that is entirely determined by genetics, identical twins would either both have the trait or both not have it.

and seeing which things seem to occur together – that other traits or features can also be inherited. In reality almost everything about us – our looks, build, temperament and health – are brought about by a combination of our genes and our environment.

Appearance and aptitudes

Genetics plays a large part in superficial aspects of the way we look, such as eye shape, height, hair colour, individual build and the way that the body is put together. But we also know that we can change many things about ourselves by modifying the environmental influences. Blondes will get blonder in strong sunshine, for example. If we eat too much we will put on weight. If we exercise we can build muscle tone.

If you have genes that incline you to be lean and muscled, it is likely that you will find it easier to be a good athlete than someone who has inherited genes that give them weak muscles and a congenital heart problem. But if you never exercise and the person with the weak muscles and heart problem does, they may become the better athlete.

Intelligence

Intelligence is extremely difficult to quantify. We know that ability with IQ tests, which test verbal and spatial reasoning, is in part determined culturally and in part is genetic. In general, a child's mental abilities fall about halfway between those of their parents, so bright parents tend to have bright children and more average parents usually have children who are closer to average in their intellectual abilities. IQ has been shown to be fairly

heritable and can determine certain abilities. However, measuring intelligence is only a part of the equation and does not determine ultimate success. Other factors such as organisational abilities, creativity, drive, support, determination and opportunity play a large part in a person's ultimate level of success. Also, it is surprisingly rare for an acknowledged 'genius' to produce another genius.

Unforeseen circumstances can also interrupt the development of a genetically normal individual. A child of very bright parents who suffers a lack of oxygen during birth, for example, may experience a degree of brain damage and do less well than a child of more average parents whose birth went well.

Learning disabilities

Learning disabilities often seem to cluster in families. The implication of the clustering is that a combination of genes and environment play a role in the development of such problems. For example, about a quarter of children diagnosed with attention deficit hyperactive disorder (ADHD) discover that one parent had characteristics and temperament that led to similar difficulties in school. Dyslexia is also often seen to cluster in families.

The endless debate concerns whether these examples of clustering imply an external or an internal cause. Is nature or nurture responsible? At present, for most of these less-defined conditions, it is hard to tell. 'Nature' advocates tend to think that genetics plays the major role, while many 'Nurture' advocates such as psychologists prefer a less deterministic view.

ATHLETIC ABILITY
Sporting ability appears to run in families; now scientists have pinpointed a 'go faster' gene that is linked to athletic aptitude.

HEIGHT
Height is heritable but the pattern of inheritance is complex. Multiple genes are involved, leading to variation in families.

HAIR COLOUR
Natural hair colour is an inherited trait, whereas dyed hair is an accquired trait. The onset and rate of greying and hair loss are mostly dictated by genetic influences.

Understanding risks to family health

Knowing the health history of your family, in particular your parents and grandparents, and whether one or more of them suffer from certain health problems, can be a good first step in determining risks for you and your children.

FAMILIAL AND GENETIC DISORDERS

When looking at the occurrence and risk of certain disorders within a family, it is important to be aware of the distinction between familial and genetically inherited disorders. These terms are often used interchangeably, but to specialists they have very different meanings.

A familial disorder is one that clusters in families. It may have a genetic component but it may also have a large environmental component. These conditions are what are known as multifactorial conditions in that they are not entirely genetic even though they appear to occur more in some families than in others.

Genetic disorders are more strictly defined as occurring as a result of a change in a gene or group of genes. It is a broad term: any disorder that is caused by a change in the genes is genetic. Not all genetic disorders are inherited, though many of them are.

FAMILY HEALTH HISTORY

The best way to look for inherited conditions is to take a family health history, which is a fundamental part of any genetic evaluation of a family or individual. A family history is a generational map – a shorthand way of mapping out the relevant information so that it can be seen at a glance. It shows up patterns of inheritance and allows a professional to assess whether there is a likelihood of inherited disease.

However, a family history is only as good as the information that the family can provide about the health of individual family members. It may take several attempts to gather the information for a complete picture, involving a dialogue between the professional interpreting the family history and the various affected family members. You can speed up the process by putting together as complete a family history as you can before visiting a professional.

Getting started

When looking at the health history of your whole family it may help to draw out a family tree. It is conventional to put the father on the left and the mother on the right and to list the siblings by age with the oldest on the left and the youngest on the right. Where there are half-siblings, make sure that they are listed in the right order. Start by adding details about your own health. Then put down details about your parents and your siblings, including their age and health. If they have had health problems write down the dates of the illnesses and how old the person was when they first developed the illness.

You will need to expand this family tree by adding your parents' siblings, their children and your parents' parents (your grandparents). Write down the age of all the individuals concerned. For the deceased, include the age at which they died and cause of death.

There are usually one or two key people in the family, often a mother or grandmother, who know a lot about the medical histories of other family members. When you prepare a family history you need to interview the family members about their health, but one way to simplify this is to start with the key people and see what they know. If this shows up a condition, such as cancer or heart disease, that you are particularly concerned about then you can ask more details about it from family members with that condition. If there is no particular condition, then think about some general health screening questions.

Asking the right questions

For specific conditions, research the illness and design a set of screening questions for it. If you are concerned about a family history of diabetes, for example, find out if it was type I or type II. When was it diagnosed and what treatment was recommended? Was it controlled by diet or by medication? Did this work or did the treatment change and when? Is the patient on insulin?

If you are dealing with an adult-onset disease like cancer or heart disease you need to know the age at diagnosis, the exact diagnosis, the age at subsequent diagnoses and, if the person is no longer living, the age at death. If treatment occurred, what did it involve and is it still continuing (or how long was it needed)? In the case of cancer, what was the site of origin of the cancer? How was the diagnosis made? Did the patient have surgery or chemotherapy or radiation therapy? Has there been a recurrence, if so where and what treatment was received?

FAMILY TRAITS

*It is possible to trace characteristics such as hair colour through a family, but many traits can
be seen to skip a generation. Some characteristics, such as weight, may have health implications.*

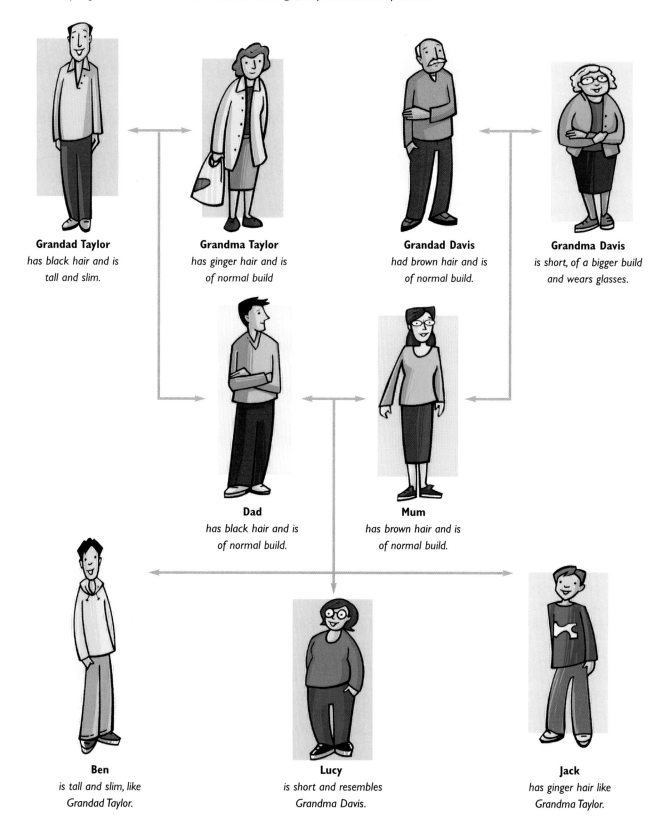

Grandad Taylor
*has black hair and is
tall and slim.*

Grandma Taylor
*has ginger hair and is
of normal build*

Grandad Davis
*had brown hair and is
of normal build.*

Grandma Davis
*is short, of a bigger build
and wears glasses.*

Dad
*has black hair and is
of normal build.*

Mum
*has brown hair and is
of normal build.*

Ben
*is tall and slim, like
Grandad Taylor.*

Lucy
*is short and resembles
Grandma Davis.*

Jack
*has ginger hair like
Grandma Taylor.*

If you are concerned about a condition diagnosed in an infant or child, you need to find out the signs and symptoms and when they first appeared. Were they present from birth, at a few months of age or later? Did the child have delays in the development of motor skills or language acquisition? If a diagnosis has already been made, what is it? Find out if a heart specialist, paediatrician or genetics department made the diagnosis and where. This will enable your GP or geneticist to get the actual medical records to confirm the diagnosis.

If it is a disorder of childhood or adolescence, at what age did the illness develop? What were the signs and symptoms? How were they first detected? Which specialists did the child see?

General questions
If there is nothing of particular concern in your family, here are some general screening questions to get you started.
• Is there anyone in your family with a mental deficiency? If so, do you know what kind and whether that person ever had a diagnosis, or reason given for their mental deficiency? How severe is it? What kinds of things can they do and what can they not do? How old are they and is there a chance that there might still be original medical records held somewhere?
• Is there anyone in your family who was born with a birth defect or something that might have needed fixing after birth, such as a heart problem or an extra finger or toe?
• Are there any women in your family who suffered two or more miscarriages? If so, were they early

The most common disease to run in Caucasian families is haemochromatosis: 1 in 10 people carry the defective gene, but fewer than 1 in 500 show symptoms.

or late miscarriages? Was there ever an explanation of the reason why they had the miscarriages?
• Was a baby ever stillborn in the family, or did a child die in infancy? If so, what of?
Other things to ask about are any developmental delays in children in the family. Were they unusually slow to walk or talk, or do they need special assistance in school? Do they have vision or hearing problems, or wheelchair need? Did anyone die prematurely, other than by accident or from an infection.

Interpreting your family history
Almost everyone has something in their family health history – in the end, people have to die of something. A family history can highlight premature deaths and other unusual events, such as handicapped babies or teenagers in wheelchairs. Other events or health conditions may be more difficult to read. Anyone with concerns should discuss them with their GP, who will decide whether referral to a hospital genetics department is appropriate.

The family history is a tool to look for patterns in a family. Geneticists focus on more than one individual with the same or related diagnoses. Many hypotheses can be drawn from a well-defined family history; often a particular syndrome may be inherited in several ways and testing may be appropriate to understand what is taking place (see pages 110–15 for more information on genetic counselling and testing).

Looking for clues and patterns
If a family history reveals occasional individuals with multiple unexplained miscarriages, children with mental deficiency, or babies born with multiple congenital abnormalities, chromosome testing may resolve whether the explanation is genetic. Individuals from families with one or more members with a known genetic disorder, such as cystic fibrosis, thalassaemia, or muscular dystrophy, may want to check out their inheritance risk.

This assessment is usually carried out by a genetic counsellor or geneticist after a full evaluation of the affected individual or their medical records and it may involve additional genetic testing. The form of inheritance may be clear from the diagnosis, or there may be several possible forms of inheritance for the condition. In these circumstances, the family history may help to determine which tests are appropriate.

Other conditions in families may be multifactorial, meaning that they have environmental and genetic components in their causes. With most adult-onset diseases, such as Alzheimer's, heart disease, cancer and diabetes, there are normal ages to succumb to these conditions and abnormal or early ages. Many of these diseases have a genetic component but also a large environmental component. If one of these diseases, such as heart disease or cancer, occurs at a much younger age than normal this is an indication that it could be genetic in origin.

Controlling risk factors

Your family health status and inheritance is only half the story in staying healthy yourself. Environmental factors can combine with a genetic predisposition to cause a problem, or act in isolation to damage an individual's health.

Once you have the outline of your health history, the next step is to find out if there were any environmental factors that may have contributed to individual health problems. Was the person a smoker, for example, or a heavy drinker? What kind of work did they do? If they had cancer, were they exposed to high levels of radiation or chemicals in their work? Did they take appropriate safety precautions? If a family member had heart disease at 40 instead of at 65, were they overweight? Were they healthy and fit and take regular exercise? Did they have high cholesterol levels? Had they ever been diagnosed with a heart murmur or rhythmic abnormality? If they were diagnosed with Alzheimer's in their 40s instead of in their 70s, did they ever experience a serious head injury? Were they exposed to neurotoxins?

MISCARRIAGES AND BIRTH DEFECTS

If someone in the family had more than two miscarriages, find out what explanation, if any, was ever found for this. Does the explanation sound reasonable in the light of today's knowledge? Did they manage to have full-term healthy pregnancies? (Three miscarriages in a family of twelve is less significant than three in a family with only one child.) Did they find a treatment that seemed to solve the problem, and if so what was it? Were there possible lifestyle reasons such as alcohol or violent abuse?

Birth defects occur because of an interruption to normal development in the womb caused either by genetic or environmental factors. Environmental causes could be mechanical, for example, a constraint or interruption to the blood supply, or chemical. Chemicals or medications that interfere with development are known as teratogens. In general, the dose and the timing of exposure during pregnancy are vital in determining the effect. Generally the most vulnerable period of a pregnancy is during embryogenesis, from the first

week after conception to the end of the first trimester. Not all women subject to teratogen exposure will have babies with birth defects, however, because each woman metabolises different substances in a different way.

There is concern for women with the condition phenylketonuria (PKU), because unless they are on a special low protein diet they make phenylketones as a by-product of metabolism. Their babies are usually genetically normal, but will be mentally deficient unless the mother can get her phenylketone levels low early in pregnancy and keep them low.

Returning to the family history, if a baby was born with a defect was it a common birth defect that was isolated to one system only, such as a clubfoot or cleft lip, which was

Reliable studies show no increased risk of miscarriage or birth defects in women who use VDUs.

Substance risks

Some chemicals can be health hazards during the course of everyday life, in the workplace or elsewhere. Others, called teratogens, are known to be potentially harmful to a fetus developing in the mother's womb and can lead to birth defects.

General health hazards		Teratogens	
Substance	Potential effect	Substance	Potential effect on fetus following exposure during pregnancy
ASBESTOS	Lung disease (Asbestosis)	LEAD	Mental deficiency
RADIATION	Cancers	PHENYLKETONES	Mental deficiency
ANAESTHESIA	Increased risk of miscarriage	LOW THYROID	Mental deficiency
ORGANIC SOLVENTS	Neurotoxicity and cancers	DIETHYLSTILBESTROL (DES)	Reproductive tract cancers in girls exposed in utero
PESTICIDES	Neurotoxicity and male cancers	WARFARIN	MCA (Multiple Congenital Anomaly); central nervous system and eye abnormalities
MINING	Silicosis	ISOTRETINOIN	MCA (Multiple Congenital Anomaly); central nervous system abnormalities; clefting; limb reduction abnormalities
LEAD	Mental deficiency	METHOTREXATE	MCA (Multiple Congenital Anomaly)
MERCURY	Neurotoxicity	ANTI-CONVULSANTS	Abnormal development and congenital heart defects
FORMALDEHYDE	Degenerative changes in the liver, kidneys, heart and brain; DNA damage	ALCOHOL (BINGE DRINKING)	Brain abnormalities; abnormal development and heart defects; cleft lip and/ or palate
HYDROCARBONS EG. BENZENE	Leukemias	SMOKING	Low birthweight babies

corrected when the baby was tiny? Or were there multiple abnormalities in different parts of the body?

Controlled and prescribed toxins

Some substances can cause mutations in genes or chromosomes in the germ line, that is in the eggs and sperm or the cells that create eggs and sperm. Such substances are usually controlled by doctors. For example, after chemotherapy treatment it is usual to counsel a man about using contraception for a specified period in case of sperm abnormalities. A woman about to have chemotherapy may be encouraged to think about egg retrieval and storage for possible family planning at a later date, if she has not yet completed her family.

Factors causing little or no harm

Radiation has mutagenic effects. However, it is important to realise that we are all exposed to a certain amount of background radiation which we cannot control – from space, for example, and from certain types of rock. X-ray investigations use carefully controlled, very low dose exposure. Ultrasound tests do not involve radiation at all and have no mutagenic effects on the genes.

There is no evidence that computer monitors or VDUs cause any damage to genes or embryos. Investigations have found no evidence of risk to male or female reproductive systems, and there is no increased incidence of miscarriages or birth defects among VDU operators compared to people doing other types of work.

HEALTHY EATING FOR LIFE

Researchers are discovering that the old adage 'you are what you eat' is indeed true. Food tastes develop and change as we grow from helpless newborn to senior citizen, but once the weaning stage has passed, the basic principles of a good diet are balance and variety.

52 *A healthy diet, with a good mix of nutrients in the right proportions, is a foundation stone of good health at any age.*

54 *There is a great deal parents can do to set their children on the road to healthy eating for the rest of their lives.*

58 *Many children take lunch rather than eating school meals. Here are some ideas to keep packed lunches nutritious and interesting.*

60 *Healthy foods are often abandoned as teens start to make their own food choices, but healthy options are good for growing young people.*

62 *Adults have many calls on their time and eating well can become less of a priority, but it is as important as ever during these years.*

65 *There is little doubt that appetite declines with age. People's tastes change, but the right food choices can help to fend off ill health.*

A healthy diet through life

No matter what your age, your body has specific dietary needs. A balanced diet is one that provides a supply of all the essential nutrients in the right quantities for health. Food should be enjoyed – it can be tasty and healthy too.

To ensure good health in the long term, it is important to maintain an active lifestyle and adopt a healthy balanced diet. There are five food groups that in greater or lesser quantities form part of a healthy balanced diet; the portion sizes listed here apply to adults.

BREAD, OTHER CEREALS AND POTATOES

This food group should form the basis of most of your meals. Rich in starchy carbohydrates, the group also includes whole-grain breakfast cereals, rice, pasta, noodles, yam and oats. These all provide rich sources of insoluble fibre, calcium, iron and B vitamins, which are needed to keep the gut, bones and blood healthy. Base your meals on starchy carbohydrates and whenever you can, use the whole-grain, wholemeal or high fibre versions. Carbohydrates provide a slow-release form of energy throughout the day. Aim to eat 5–11 portions a day.

FRUITS AND VEGETABLES

Fruits and vegetables are important sources of antioxidant nutrients, such as vitamin C and beta-carotene (the vegetable equivalent of vitamin A), offering protection from cancers and heart disease. They are rich in soluble fibre, which can help to lower blood cholesterol. Frozen, canned and dried versions, as well as juices, offer the same health benefits as fresh fruits and vegetables. Try to eat at least five portions each day.

MILK AND DAIRY FOODS

This group provides an excellent source of essential nutrients such as calcium, zinc, protein, vitamins A, D, B_2 and B_{12}, which are important for maintaining healthy bones, skin and blood. Try to include a couple of servings from this food group each day, choosing low-fat versions of milk, yoghurt, cheese and fromage frais whenever possible. Bio-yoghurts are excellent for intestinal health.

MEAT, FISH AND ALTERNATIVES

The main nutrients supplied by this food group include iron, protein, B vitamins, zinc and magnesium, which are needed to maintain healthy blood and efficient functioning of the immune system. Choose a maximum of two servings from this group each day from chicken, lean red meat (venison is an excellent low-fat red

What is a portion?

A well-balanced diet, comprising all the major food groups, will help to ensure a wide range of valuable nutrients, vitamins and minerals, each day. Here are some examples of what a portion means in each food group:

Carbohydrates
One portion is equivalent to:
- 1 medium potato
- 1 small pitta bread
- 1 bagel
- 3 tbsp wheatflakes or branflakes
- 1 whole-wheat biscuit
- 2 tbsp cooked sweet potato
- 2 tbsp uncooked oats or muesli
- 3 crackers or crispbread

Fruit
One portion is equivalent to:
- 1 slice of melon or pineapple
- ½ avocado or grapefruit
- 1 banana, pear, apple or orange
- 2 small pieces of fruit, such as plums, clementines, apricots or kiwi fruit
- 1 cup of grapes or berries
- 2–3 tbsp canned fruit or fruit salad
- 1 tbsp dried fruit, such as dates
- 150ml pure fruit juice

meat), fish, turkey, eggs and nuts. Beans and pulses such as kidney, haricot, soya, broad beans, pinto beans and lentils are great protein alternatives, as is tofu or soya bean curd, which has the added bonus of being an excellent source of calcium.

A HEALTHY FLUID INTAKE

Fluid lost from the body through perspiration, urination or aspiration must be replaced. An average adult needs around 1.5 litres of fluid a day (more on the hottest summer days), which is equivalent to around 8 glasses of water. Fluids include water, fruit juice, milk and fruit or herbal teas, as well as reduced sugar soft drinks. Weak tea and coffee also count but only in moderation as they have a diuretic effect and can encourage further loss of fluids.

FOODS TO RESTRICT

Beware of processed foods which can contain a lot of sugar and fat. Try to minimise your intake of foods such as savoury snacks, biscuits, cakes, crisps, pastries, sweets, chocolate, pies, butter and carbonated drinks.

Salt

Our physiological need for sodium is small. We only need 1.6g sodium a day – the equivalent to the amount of salt in two slices of bread. Data from a government survey on the diets of British adults indicate that we eat far more than we need.

There are concerns that high intakes of sodium may have adverse effects on blood pressure, which has implications for hypertension and other illnesses such as heart disease and stroke. The Department of Health in 1994 recommended that the UK population should cut the average intake of salt from 9g a day (equivalent to 3.5g of sodium) to 6g a day (equivalent to 2g of sodium). The recommendation was based on studies showing that this could reduce blood pressure in older people and others with high blood pressure.

- Avoid excessive quantities of tinned vegetables, salted butter, margarine and spreads, cheese, bread, ready meals, pizza, pies, crisps and certain breakfast cereals (check the sodium content on the label). Processed meats such as bacon, sausages, other types of meat products like luncheon meat, seasonings such as monosodium glutamate (MSG), sodium bicarbonate and some antacid medicines should be consumed in moderation. All contain high amounts of salt.
- Don't use salt at the table.
- Reduce the amount of salt used in cooking by trying alternative seasonings such as herbs and spices, lime juice and lemon juice.
- Do not add salt to children's foods.
- Buy low-sodium versions of foods and condiments like Lo-salt, or use shoyu instead of soy sauce.

Vegetables
One portion is equivalent to:
- 2 tbsp broccoli, courgettes, spinach, cabbage, carrots, turnips, peas, sweet corn, mushrooms or onion
- 1 medium-sized bowl of salad

Meat, fish and alternatives
One portion is equivalent to:
- 3 tbsp cooked beans or lentils
- 50–90g lean meat, poultry or oily fish
- 70g cooked lamb's liver
- 1 boiled egg
- 100–150g white fish
- 2 tbsp nuts or peanut butter

Milk and dairy foods
One portion is equivalent to:
- ⅓ pint (200 ml) milk
- 125g pot of yoghurt or fromage frais
- 25g hard cheese
- 100g cottage cheese

A healthy diet for babies and children

All parents wish their children to be healthy and there's a great deal you can do to give your child the best start in life. A child's diet needs special care and planning – energy and nutrient requirements are high, but appetites are small.

THE FIRST FEW MONTHS

While baby formula will supply a baby's nutritional needs, studies have shown that breastfeeding is best for babies, offering many advantages to a newly born infant and the mother. The act of breastfeeding strengthens the bond between the mother and baby. It is hygienic and milk is always available and at the correct temperature for the baby. It also helps utilise excess fat stored in the mother's body during pregnancy. Furthermore, breast milk is free; baby formula on the other hand must be purchased. Powdered or liquid concentrate baby formula also must be mixed with water, which can be time consuming. For the baby, from a nutritional viewpoint, breast milk:

- is a complete food, providing all the necessary nutrients – no additional nutrients are required until the baby reaches about six months of age;
- contains fatty acids needed for brain and eye development;
- contains antibodies offering protection against many types of bacterial and viral infections;
- protects against the development of allergies.

However, breastfeeding does have certain disadvantages. The mother has to be available 24 hours a day during the early weeks to feed the baby while breastfeeding is being established. Establishing breastfeeding can be problematic and sometimes the mother will suffer discomfort, engorgement and sore nipples. It is difficult to gauge how much milk the baby is drinking, although feeding 'on demand' should ensure that the baby is getting enough. Mothers may be embarrassed about or discouraged from breastfeeding in public. And partners and siblings can become jealous of the close relationship between a breastfeeding mother and her baby.

The Department of Health in the UK and the World Health Organization encourage mothers to breastfeed their babies exclusively for the first 4–6 months of life and to wait until then before introducing solids. This advice is based on studies which have found that babies who are breastfed have a lower risk of gastro-enteritis and respiratory and ear infections. In addition, children who are breastfed may be at lower risk of becoming obese later in childhood. There is also evidence that there may be long-term benefits for mothers. A study published in the *Lancet* in 2002 found that among 150,000 women studied, the longer they breastfed the more protection they had against breast cancer.

Bottlefeeding

Some mothers cannot or do not want to breastfeed for many reasons. Breastfeeding may be difficult to establish or a woman may need to return to work and therefore cannot be available to breastfeed at all times. Mothers should not feel guilty about not breastfeeding. As long as good hygiene practices are followed a baby should thrive on formula. Feeds must be made up exactly as instructed on the pack and bottles and utensils used must be sterilised. Most importantly, infant formula should never be too concentrated – an infant's kidneys are immature and cannot adapt to high concentrations of protein and minerals.

WEANING

At around four to six months, the nutrient stores that an infant had at birth gradually decline and milk alone is no longer sufficient to meet their nutrient and energy requirements. Furthermore, an infant's iron stores start to become depleted at around six months, so additional sources of iron need to be added into the diet. This is when

Safe salt levels for children
In 2003, the Foods Standards Agency issued salt intake targets for children. Recommendations on the maximum levels of salt that should be eaten per day are given below:

AGE	MAXIMUM SALT PER DAY
0–6 months	less than 1g
7–12 months	1g
1–3 years	2g
4–6 years	3g
7–10 years	5g
11–14 years	6g

Making the transition
The milestone of feeding solid foods is an exciting one. It heralds an important marker in the first year of development.

solid foods should be introduced. If breastfeeding, weaning is often easier if a child has taken milk from a source other than the breast – for example, the occasional bottle of breast milk from around four months.

Getting started with solid foods

The Department of Health's advice is to start weaning from six months, but talk to your health visitor if you're unsure. Initially the process of weaning involves getting the baby used to the idea of a spoon. Ideal foods to start with are baby rice, pureed vegetables such as potato or carrot, or pureed non-citrus fruits such as apple, banana or pear. Start with one teaspoon during a breast or bottle feed once a day. Cow's milk should not be added to a baby's food under the age of six months and should not be given as a drink until the child is at least one year old.

Six months

At this time, aim to introduce new tastes to the baby and to provide additional nutrients. In addition to baby rice, vegetables and fruits, you could try pureed meat, such as chicken or liver, pureed pulses such as lentils and plain yoghurt. Aim for 1–2 teaspoons during two milk feeds a day, progressing to during three milk feeds a day.

Six to nine months

At this time, aim to help the baby to gain independence from milk as the main source of nutrition. Ideal foods include cereals containing wheat or a little citrus fruit such as an orange. The baby can also try whatever the rest of the family is having, as long as no salt, sugar or spices have been added. Good examples of such meals would be cauliflower cheese or cottage pie, thoroughly cooked eggs, fish, cheese or fromage frais.

Introduce wheat, eggs and fish one at a time so that if there is an allergic reaction, you can tell what caused it. Foods offered to the baby should still be mashed to a smooth consistency but can contain a few soft lumps. Once the child can chew well enough to minimise the risk of choking, finger foods can be introduced, including pitta bread, breadsticks, banana, pieces of carrot and apple.

Solid foods should be given 3–5 times a day before a milk feed. The amount given will depend on the size of the baby's appetite. As babies take more solids, they are likely to want less milk at each feed.

Nine months to one year

During this period a baby's ability to chew improves. They are now ready to learn how to feed themselves.

Ideal foods should include an increased variety of tastes and textures. The baby can share the family meal such as lamb or beef casserole with vegetables or chicken with noodles as long as no salt, sugar or spices have been added. Foods should still be mashed or chopped.

HANDY HINTS FOR FUSSY EATERS

- Don't overwhelm a child with a large amount of food on the plate. Serve small portions.
- Praise children when they finish their food.
- If food is rejected, don't make a fuss, just clear the food away.
- Try not to use food as rewards.
- Avoid too many snacks during the day: children get too full to eat their main meal.
- If a child dislikes fruit and vegetables, try mixing them with foods they do like, such as potatoes, baby rice or yoghurt.
- Offer new foods alongside familiar ones.

Distribute food over three meals plus two snacks a day. You can increase the serving size as the baby's appetite grows. Aim to give 500ml breast milk or formula either as a drink on its own or mixed with fruit.

Suitable drinks

Infants and young children need sufficient fluids for their bodies to function properly and to prevent constipation. Cooled, boiled water can be offered to bottle-fed babies, particularly in hot weather, while breast-fed babies can be offered the breast more frequently if they appear thirsty. Once the diet becomes more varied, diluted fruit juices can be given. Cow's milk is okay after 12 months, but reduced-fat milk should not be given as a drink until the child is at least two years old, after which semi-skimmed can be offered, as long as the child is eating well.

Offer children drinks from a cup rather than a bottle. Fruit juices and squashes, carbonated drinks and flavoured milks contain a type of sugar that can damage a child's teeth if it remains in contact for too long. They may also contain an artificial sweetener called cyclamate (E953) and young children should have no more than three 180ml cups a day of diluted soft drinks and squashes that contain this. Always dilute drinks for children more than you would for an adult.

VEGETARIAN OR VEGAN DIETS

After weaning, careful planning is essential if an infant or child is to be fed a vegetarian or vegan diet. It is important that children are not given too much fibre and that they get enough iron, calcium, protein, vitamin B_{12} and zinc in their diet.

For a vegetarian, this means giving children milk, cheese, eggs, beans, lentils, green leafy vegetables and yeast extracts. For vegan diets, soya-based infant formulas can be used initially followed by soya drinks (with added calcium), fortified baby and breakfast cereals, breads, pulses, lentils, beans, dried fruit, green leafy vegetables, tofu, tempeh, soya mince, soya cheese and some yeast extract after weaning. Seek medical advice, as vitamin and mineral supplements may be needed in addition.

Here are some examples of meals that a family can share:
- Couscous with peas and carrots.
- Vegetable risotto made with risotto rice, a touch of milk (soya milk, if vegan) and a variety of vegetables like carrots, onions and broccoli.
- Neapolitan pasta with chickpea, onion and tomato sauce.

The principles of a healthy balanced diet for adults also apply to children. It is important to remember, however, that children under two years of age have a small stomach capacity. This means that they need nutrient- and energy-dense foods provided in small quantities, such as full-fat milk (after one year of age) and dairy products. There is no need to worry too much about children eating too much fat because they need the extra calories. High fibre foods should be limited because these are too bulky for a child's stomach to cope with.

GROWING NEEDS

The energy requirements of children are high in relation to their size. Children's bodies grow rapidly and they become more and more active with age. Energy and nutrient-dense foods served in small, frequent meals

Dealing with food allergies

Children from a family with a history of allergies are more likely to have allergies themselves. It is important to consult the doctor or health visitor if you notice a pattern of adverse reactions in your child after ingesting certain foods. Do not simply restrict such foods without expert assessment as you may inadvertently cause nutrient deficiencies.

Foods that tend to provoke an allergic reaction include cow's milk, fish, wheat, eggs, shellfish, nuts and peanuts. Typical symptoms include coughing, wheezing, skin rashes, vomiting, diarrhoea and a runny nose and eyes. Sometimes symptoms can be severe, even life threatening. For example, children with a peanut allergy may suffer anaphylactic shock if they consume any food containing traces of peanuts. If you suspect your child may have a peanut allergy or peanut allergy runs in your family, seek medical advice.

ASK THE EXPERT

are the best way to keep up with the nutritional requirements of a growing child.

Young children need protein, calcium, iron and vitamins A and D to support their growth and energy requirements. Calcium and vitamin

Together at the table
When families eat together, they're more likely to enjoy a healthy variety of foods and to find time to talk to each other.

D are also needed for the development of healthy and strong teeth and bones. They also need to have an adequate intake of fibre, folate (one of the B vitamins), vitamins B_6, B_{12} and E.

It is important to make sure that your child gets sufficient iron during this rapid growth stage. A lack of iron can result in iron-deficiency anaemia, which leaves a child susceptible to frequent infections, slow or poor weight gain and delays in development. Iron-rich foods include lean red meat such as lamb and beef, and liver. For children on a vegetarian diet, dark green leafy vegetables, nuts, pulses, dried fruits and some fortified breakfast cereals should be included on a daily basis. Aim for a couple of portions a day. Vegetable sources of iron are not absorbed as well by the body. However, having a rich supply of vitamin C, such as a glass of orange juice, with the meal enhances the body's ability to take up iron from vegetable sources.

HEALTHY EATING GUIDELINES

Children over five years of age begin to take responsibility for their own food intake, so it is important that they understand the need for a healthy diet. However, family life early on will have influenced their eating habits, and it is difficult to

change these once established. The best start for a child is if the whole family has a healthy lifestyle.

A study published in the *Archives of Family Medicine* found that having a family supper was associated with a more healthy way of eating. Furthermore, it found that if a family sits down to have a meal together it can have a positive effect on the family's emotional health as well. The study looked at the relationship between family dinners and the quality of diet among thousands of children in the United States. Although more than half of the nine-year-olds surveyed said they had a family dinner every day, this practice seemed to decline as children got older. Only one-third of children aged 14 reported having dinner regularly with their families.

The study found that those who regularly ate dinner with their families were more likely to have eaten at least five portions of fruit and vegetables. They also had fewer fried foods and soft drinks during dinner than those children who had infrequent meals with their family did. Eating together also fosters family conversation and healthier attitudes to food and body image.

Nutritious school lunches

School meals make a vital contribution to the daily energy and nutrient intake of children. Sandwiches are the most common packed lunch, but to encourage variety once or twice a week you could substitute sandwiches with one of the following easy-to-make recipes.

The recipes here can be made as evening meals and the leftovers will be delicious to eat the next day. Children should also be given a carton or bottle of fruit juice, milk or water.

VEGETARIAN SNACKS

If you provide children with interesting nutritious choices when it comes to snacking, they will enjoy eating healthily. Here are some suggestions:

Potato wedges with yoghurt dip
Vegetable samosa
Cheese and tomato mini-pizza
Vegetarian spring roll
Boiled egg
Handful of nuts, seeds or dried fruit
Piece of fresh fruit
Small bowl of fruit salad
Small tub of yoghurt
Portion of frozen yoghurt or
    low-fat ice cream
Cereal bar
Piece of vegetarian cheese
Raw vegetable sticks and dips
Vegetable soup

SPINACH AND RICOTTA QUICHE

125g wholemeal flour
50g margarine
2–3 tbsp cold water
200g cooked spinach
200g ricotta cheese
200ml milk
2 medium eggs
Pinch of nutmeg, salt and white pepper
    to taste
150g Gruyere cheese, grated

Preheat the oven to 200°C/400°F/ gas mark 6. Sift the flour into a bowl. Rub in the margarine and add suffient water to bind. Roll out on a lightly floured surface and use to line a greased 20-cm quiche dish or flan ring. Bake the pastry case blind for 10–12 minutes. Remove from the oven and reduce the heat to 180°C/350°F/gas mark 4.

Combine the spinach and ricotta cheese in a bowl and place the mixture into the base of the pastry case. Whisk the milk and the eggs together and season to taste with nutmeg, salt and pepper.

Pour the egg mixture into the pastry case. Sprinkle over with Gruyere cheese and place on a baking tray in the oven for 30–40 minutes or until the filling has set. Serve with sliced tomatoes.

POTATO AND MUSHROOM FRITTATA

2 tbsp olive oil
1 medium onion, finely sliced
180g peeled potatoes, finely sliced
150g mushrooms, sliced
3 large eggs, whisked slightly
2 tbsp fresh parsley, chopped
Salt and pepper to taste

Heat the oil in a non-stick pan. Add the onion, potatoes and mushrooms and brown for a few minutes. Turn the heat down and cook gently for 20 minutes until the vegetables have softened, stirring from time to time.

In a bowl, combine the eggs, parsley and seasoning and pour into the pan. Cook on a low heat for 15–20 minutes or until the eggs have nearly set. Towards the end of the cooking time, preheat the grill.

Place the pan under the grill and cook until the top has set. Leave the frittata to cool and then chill it. Serve with cucumber, tomato and bread.

CRUNCHY LENTIL SALAD

175g green lentils
1 litre vegetable stock
1 medium onion, finely chopped
75g carrots, grated
1 red apple, diced
1 tbsp fresh parsley, finely chopped
1 tbsp olive oil
1 tbsp balsamic vinegar
150g feta cheese, crumbled
25g dried raisins
Salt and pepper to taste

Place the lentils and stock in a pan, bring to the boil, cover and simmer for 30–35 minutes or until the lentils are tender. Drain well and cool. Mix the lentils with the onion, carrots, apple, parsley, olive oil and vinegar, and season to taste. Mix in the feta cheese and dried raisins and adjust seasoning. Serve with boiled new potatoes.

PASTA SALAD

250g penne or farfalle pasta

3 tbsp olive oil

2 tbsp tomato juice

1½ tbsp lime juice

1 tbsp fresh dill, chopped

12 cherry tomatoes, halved

125g black olives

200g cooked peeled prawns

1 spring onion, finely chopped

Black pepper to taste

Cook the pasta according to the pack instructions. For the dressing whisk together the olive oil, tomato juice, lime juice and dill. Drain the cooked pasta and mix with the tomatoes, olives, prawns and spring onion. Pour on the dressing, mix gently and serve.

positive health tips

Interesting fillings for appetising sandwiches:

- Peanut butter and sliced banana
- Cream cheese with dried raisins and pecans
- Sliced mozzarella cheese and sliced tomato
- Cooked chicken with sliced avocado
- Turkey with cranberry sauce and sliced cucumber
- Tinned sardines and chopped cucumber
- Hummus with grated carrot

FRUITY CHICKEN SALAD WITH RICE

250g brown rice, cooked

12 dried apricots, chopped

50g toasted almonds

½ bulb fennel, sliced

1 tbsp mango chutney

Juice of 1 lime

4 cooked chicken breasts, diced

1 cucumber, diced

125g Greek yoghurt

2 tbsp fresh coriander, chopped

Salt and pepper to taste

Mix all the ingredients together in a large bowl and season to taste.

A healthy diet for teenagers

Eating becomes a social activity for teenagers and peers have a great influence on what their friends eat. As teenagers tend to eat a lot of junk food and often do not fulfil their daily nutrient requirements, home meals should be healthy.

What your child eats now can have an impact on health in later years. There is scientific evidence from some studies to suggest that the process of certain diseases can be traced back to childhood weight, cholesterol levels and blood pressure.

During adolescence (approximately 10–18 years), young people require an increase in the amount of energy and nutrients in their diet. This is particularly true for boys because the rate at which their height increases is greater than in girls. This increase in height in boys is also accompanied by an increase in the growth of muscles. However, bone density increases quickly for both boys and girls during adolescence and should be supported by eating healthily.

EXTRA ENERGY

Average energy and nutrient requirements for those aged between 11 and 14 are 2200 calories for boys and 1845 calories for girls. Older boys need even more energy. Between the ages of 15 and 18 boys have a daily requirement of 2755 calories compared to 2110 calories for girls in the same age group.

A healthy diet for a teenager should be based on as wide a variety of foods as possible. Because their nutrient and energy requirements are high compared to their body size, they need nutrient and energy-dense foods.

SOCIAL INFLUENCES

Many social influences affect what teenagers will eat, but perhaps the most pervasive, particularly among girls, is the pressure to be slim. Glossy magazines and other media pump out messages about how to

Estimates suggest that a third of teenagers skip breakfast, with girls being the worst offenders. Thinner girls are more likely to eat breakfast than overweight ones.

achieve a 'perfect' body, promoting images of unhealthily slim celebrities as an example to be followed. The government survey (see Talking Point, left) showed that 16 per cent of all girls aged 15–18 were currently dieting to lose weight compared with 3 per cent of boys in the same age group. Dr Andrew Hill, a senior lecturer in psychology at the University of Leeds, has found girls as young as nine who are restrained eaters and report frequent bouts of dieting. The implication is that if a child is not overweight or obese but still imposes diet restrictions on herself it may lead to anorexia or bulimia nervosa. So the emphasis on healthy nutrition needs to be put in context to ensure that it doesn't enhance the culture of weight loss, which tips the balance in favour of eating disorders that could lead to serious illnesses and, in some cases, premature death.

Slimming diets often encourage the exclusion of 'fattening' foods such as potatoes, bread, cereals, pasta, meat, milk and dairy products. Eliminating such foods has serious implications for the intake of carbohydrate, fibre, iron, calcium and other vitamins and minerals, which help to maintain health, prevent constipation and avoid diseases such as anaemia and, later in life, osteoporosis.

Parents, schools, government and the media should consistently deliver not just a message about the benefits of a varied and balanced diet but also about the importance of physical activity in a healthy lifestyle. Food manufacturers, caterers and retailers should be encouraged to develop products that help to support the messages of healthy nutrition. Of course knowing what teenagers

should be eating and getting them to put it into practice can be two very different things. As adolescence progresses, parental influence tends to decline whilst that of friends, peers and media-led fashions take over. Developing independence often leads to adolescents rebelling over what is eaten within the family setting, which may also be coupled with a refusal to eat anything that their parents or teachers consider to be 'healthy'. 'Junk foods' are often associated with independence, friends and fun.

Teens and vitamin supplements

As long as young people are eating a varied and balanced diet and they are not losing weight, vitamin supplements are usually not necessary. However, a multivitamin with minerals can help to fill in nutritional gaps caused by irregular eating habits. Adolescent girls are more vulnerable to iron deficiency because of higher physiological needs and menstrual losses, so teenage girls may need iron supplements. They may also need a daily calcium supplement to help protect against osteoporosis in later life.

A healthy day

In some respects, the nutrient and energy needs of teenagers are higher than those of any other age group. Young people have large appetites and it's important they eat food of high nutritional value in well-balanced meals rather than too many snacks that are rich in fat, sugar or salt.

Here are some quick and tasty suggestions:

BREAKFAST
Bowl of whole-grain cereal, topped with fruit, served with reduced-fat milk
Glass of fruit juice
1–2 slices of wholemeal bread with low-fat spread and marmalade

LUNCH
Lean hamburger in a bun
Bowl of salad
Pot of reduced-fat yoghurt
Apple

DINNER
Wholewheat spaghetti with bolognese sauce
Boiled carrots and peas
Banana with custard

QUICK AND EASY SNACKS
Glass of semi-skimmed milk
2 digestive biscuits
Fruit smoothie
Peanut butter and banana sandwich
Vegetable sticks with cottage cheese dip
Fortified breakfast cereals with semi-skimmed milk
Dried fruit
Nuts and seeds
Fruit yoghurt or fromage frais
Bagel with cucumber and cream cheese
Glass of fruit juice
Wholemeal scone with jam
Flapjack
Baked beans on wholemeal toast

A healthy diet for adults

The foods we eat can have a huge impact on our health. Healthy eating provides all the necessary nutrients to create and repair tissues, to sustain a healthy immune system, and to enable the body to undertake daily tasks with ease.

For young adults, the pressures of climbing the career ladder combined with a hectic social life – and perhaps a young family – often means that getting a balanced meal and a good night's sleep can be difficult. Yet it's important for young adults to try to eat healthily since this is the period when the body stores up vitamins and minerals that could prevent illness in later life.

By the time we hit our forties and fifties, we're at risk of over-nutrition rather than under-nutrition. This is not necessarily because we eat more but because our lives are more settled, we become less physically active, the metabolism slows and we require fewer calories than we did in the past. At this time of life, a woman's energy requirement is around 1940 calories a day, depending on her lifestyle, whereas a man's requirement is around 2550 calories.

FAT IN THE DIET

At least half of the population in the UK today, both male and female, is overweight or obese. Most health experts agree that this extra weight is caused simply by eating more calories than we need.

Diets high in fat are high in calories. In its 1995 report on obesity, the Department of Health suggested that excess energy from carbohydrates is more likely to be burned up as energy, whereas excess fat in the diet tends to be stored in the body as fat.

Our daily requirement for fat is around 75g for an adult woman and 90g for an adult man. Most of us exceed those targets every day, which has implications for obesity. In addition, most adults are also eating too much saturated fat, which can increase the risk of diseases like heart disease, diabetes, gallbladder disease, respiratory problems and some cancers. Avoiding high-fat foods is important and reducing saturated fats, such as those found in full-fat milk and dairy products, and meat, is a good start.

However, you still need to keep some fat in your diet, not least because fat contains important nutrients like vitamin E, which protects against heart disease. Some types of fats are healthy, including those found in oily fish like trout, salmon, mackerel and sardines. Great alternatives to using hard fats such as butter and lard in cooking include olive oil, sunflower or safflower oil and reduced-fat spreads containing olive oil.

30–45 YEARS

Pregnancy and folate

More women are choosing to wait until they are in their thirties or even early forties to have children. Vitamin intake is important for all would-be mothers, but for this older age group it is even more so.

The pre-conception diet should be especially rich in folate, one of the B vitamins – folic acid is the synthetic form of this vitamin. Folic acid and folate are essential building blocks for new cells and there is now considerable evidence to suggest that folic acid is crucial prior to and early in pregnancy to help protect against neural tube defects in the fetus. It is advisable for all women planning a pregnancy to supplement their diet with 400 ug (0.4 mg) of folic acid a day from three months prior to conception until the twelfth week of pregnancy. Folate occurs in vegetables such as broccoli, spinach, Brussel sprouts and peas. Oranges, yeast extract, potatoes, pulses and fortified breads and breakfast cereals are also good sources and should be included in the diet as well. The recommended daily amount for folate for non-pregnant adult women is 200 ug.

VITAMIN B$_{12}$

This vitamin is needed to prevent anaemia. Vitamin B$_{12}$ is found mainly in animals and animal products. Plant foods usually don't have appreciable amounts, but other good sources include fortified yeast extract, fortified soya milk, fortified breakfast cereals and fortified textured vegetable protein (TVP). Vegetarians who eat a balanced diet including dairy products usually do not need to worry about vitamin deficiencies. Vegans, however, may have to work harder to get enough of vitamins B$_{12}$, B$_2$, D and iron.

VITAMIN B$_2$

Vitamin B$_2$, also called riboflavin, is found in liver, fish, cheese, eggs and milk products. Good vegan sources of riboflavin include yeast extract, fortified or whole-grain breakfast cereals, seaweed, avocado and seeds such as sesame or sunflower. It is also in green leafy vegetables, pulses and yoghurt.

VITAMIN D

This vitamin is essential to enabling the body to absorb calcium from the gut and to help deposit it in the skeleton. Our main source of vitamin D is through the action of sunlight on the skin. For most people, except those who are housebound or those in communities wearing all-enveloping clothes, a small amount of exposure is more than enough. Vitamin D is also found in meat and meat products, egg yolk and oily fish such as herring, salmon and trout. Fortified breakfast cereals, fortified soya milk, soya cheese and vegan margarines also contain a good amount. Strict vegans who don't get enough sun may need supplements.

A healthy day for adults

For good all-round health and to help reduce your risk or heart disease and certain cancers you should eat a well-balanced diet. This means a balance of carbohydrates, protein, fibre, vitamins, minerals and fat.

BREAKFAST
Half a grapefruit
Bowl of porridge with sliced banana and reduced-fat milk
Glass of orange juice

LUNCH
Wholemeal pitta bread with reduced-fat hummus and grated carrots
Reduced-fat fruit yoghurt
Fruit salad

DINNER
Grilled salmon steak with boiled new potatoes
Bowl of green salad with reduced-fat dressing
Fruit sorbet

SNACKS
Fruit
Breadsticks
Fruit scone
Rye crispbread topped with cottage cheese and pineapple
Pumpernickel bread with lemon curd

A healthy day for vegans

It is important to get enough protein into a vegan diet, so eat between two and three portions of nuts, peas, lentils, tofu or beans every day. Try to eat three to five portions of bread, breakfast cereal, rice, pasta, wheat or millet. Vegans, like everyone else, should eat at least five portions of fruit and vegetables. Also, try to fit in three portions of soya milk.

BREAKFAST
Two Weetabix with a handful of strawberries and fortified soya milk
Wholemeal bread with vegan margarine
Glass of orange juice

LUNCH
Bowl of lentil and vegetable soup
Whole-grain bagel with vegan cheese and cucumber
Fortified soya yoghurt
Orange

DINNER
Tofu and vegetable curry with brown rice or quinoa
Soaked dried fruit sprinkled with muesli and topped with fortified soya yoghurt

SNACKS
Fruit
Handful of sesame or pumpkin seeds
Pumpernickel bread with peanut butter

TALKING POINT

Cutting calories to live longer

In the early 1930s scientist Clive McKay, working at Cornell University, studied the effects of calorific restriction in rodents and found that it could slow the ageing process. Since then, a great deal of research has amassed showing that a significantly reduced calorific intake in animals delays ageing and many ageing-related diseases. As we grow older, our nervous, hormonal and immune systems start to wind down and decay, and there is data to suggest that obesity can have an effect on the way that these systems function. Application of these findings to humans suggests that a reduced-calorie diet may help to set our 'neuro-endocrine' clock back to a more youthful level thereby protecting against obesity as well as against the effects of ageing. The findings do not encourage fasting, but suggest cutting daily calories intake.

IRON

There are two types of iron: haem iron comes mainly from meats and offal, while non-haem iron is found in cereals, pulses, eggs, vegetables, fruit and dairy products. Haem iron is absorbed easily by the body compared to non-haem iron, which is why there is a greater risk of iron deficiency among vegetarians. Furthermore, plant foods and whole-grain cereals contain compounds called phytates that combine with iron and make it unavailable for absorption, which puts vegans at even greater risk of deficiency. Tannins in tea also reduce the absorption of iron. However, including orange juice or a vitamin-rich food with a meal rather than having tea will help to increase the absorption of non-haem iron.

Women need larger amounts of iron to replace menstrual losses, so it's especially important to eat iron-rich foods like beans, pulses, offal, meat, dark green leafy vegetables, fortified breakfast cereals and bread. Dark chocolate, dried fruit, eggs and oysters provide useful amounts too.

CALCIUM

From birth until around the age of 30, calcium is constantly being deposited in the body. But from then on calcium starts to be lost faster from the body than it can be replaced. This increases the risk of osteoporosis in later life, when the bones become brittle and easily broken. You can protect yourself from bone loss by consuming more milk, cheese, yoghurt, bread, vegetables and fish with bones. Reduced-fat milk contains the same amount of calcium as whole milk. Calcium-fortified soya milk, orange juice, tofu and tempeh are important sources of calcium for both vegetarians and vegans.

FIBRE

Fibre keeps the gut healthy and reduces blood cholesterol levels. The average diet in the UK contains around 12g fibre, which falls below the daily recommended amount of 18g. There are two types of fibre, insoluble and soluble. Insoluble fibre helps to prevent constipation and is found in whole grains, potatoes, bran-based cereals, muesli, wholemeal bread, granary bread, whole-wheat pasta and brown rice. Soluble fibre reduces cholesterol and can be found in pulses and beans, such as lentils, black eye and red kidney beans, which protect against some cancers and heart disease.

PHYTOCHEMICALS

Many non-nutrients contained in plants have been shown to have positive health benefits. Lycopene, which is found in high levels in tomato products such as tomato ketchup, canned tomatoes and tomato soup, has been shown to reduce the risk of heart disease. Other phytochemical compounds are flavonoids. They are found in fruits, vegetables, nuts, seeds, tea, onions and apples.

ANTIOXIDANTS

Antioxidants, which include selenium and vitamins A, C and E are of vital importance in the fight against free radicals and ageing. Free radicals are produced during the normal process of metabolism, but they are also caused by a diet high in fried and barbecued foods, as well as environmental factors such as pollution, smoking and herbicides. Normally the body can handle free radicals, but if antioxidants are unavailable, or if the free radical activity becomes excessive, damage will occur. Of particular importance is that free radical damage accumulates with age.

Good sources of vitamin A include fresh fruit and vegetables, while nuts, seeds and oils provide excellent sources of vitamin E. Vitamin C is found in citrus fruits, potatoes, broccoli and Brussels sprouts.

A healthy diet in old age

Our bodies change as we age, and this can affect our dietary requirements. Changes to taste buds, lowered metabolism and a loss of appetite can mean that eating well can be a challenge, but it is essential to maintain a nutrient-rich diet.

As we get older, our nutrient stores are more likely to run low. In addition, our calorie requirements also drop. For men, requirements fall from around 2550 calories a day at the age of 50, to 2380 at 60. By the age of 75 it will be down to 2100. A woman's calorie needs also reduce, but less drastically – from 1900 a day at 50, down to 1810 after 75 years of age. This means that nutrient-rich, low-calorie foods are what is needed.

VITAL NUTRIENTS IN LATER LIFE

The stronger your bones are the more mobile and active you'll stay for the rest of your life. However, as we age our bones become thinner and our chances of developing osteoporosis (brittle bone disease) increase, especially for women. Vitamin D and calcium are important because together they enhance bone health. Vitamin D – primarily formed by the action of sunlight on the skin – enables the body to absorb calcium from food, which is then deposited on the skeleton, strengthening the bones. Vitamin D is also found in meat, oily fish, dairy and low-fat spreads, fortified breakfast cereals and eggs.

In the early years after the menopause, increasing the amount of calcium you eat will not stop bone loss from certain parts of the body altogether, but in later menopause doses of up to 500mg of calcium a day may stop bone loss from the spine and forearm. Speak to your GP about calcium supplements and remember to consume at least two portions of milk and dairy products (such as milk, yoghurt and cheese) a day. Other sources of calcium include canned fish with bones, white bread, green leafy vegetables and tofu. Hard water, fortified soya milk and fortified orange juice also provide useful amounts.

Keeping up your intake of folate, vitamin B_{12} and vitamin B_6 will reduce your chances of heart disease, strokes and anaemia. Good sources of folate include green leafy vegetables, offal, yeast extract, fortified bread and fortified breakfast cereals. The richest source of vitamin B_{12} is liver but useful amounts can be found in eggs, meat, milk, fish, fortified breakfast cereals and yeast. A wide variety of foods, including meat, fish, eggs, cereals and some vegetables such as peas and sprouts, are sources of vitamin B_6. B vitamins are also important for general health and well-being because they protect against mental and nervous problems.

The risk of cardiovascular diseases also increases with age. One way of guarding against this is to watch out for the amount and types of fat you eat. Cutting down on fat, especially saturated fats, is important. You should try to eat reduced-fat versions of meat and meat products, milk and dairy products. There is increasing evidence from scientific studies that a good intake of a type of fat called omega-3 polyunsaturated fats can reduce the risk of heart disease. You can obtain this fat from oily fish, such as mackerel, salmon, pilchards and trout.

positive health tips

Maintaining fibre and fluid intake

Fibre can help to lower blood cholesterol, protect against bowel disease and is beneficial for dealing with constipation. The daily requirement of 18g may be difficult for some older people to obtain if they can't eat a lot of food due to ill health or fewer teeth. Bran has often been used by some people to combat this problem, but there is now evidence that a compound called phytate in bran can bind to minerals such as calcium, iron and zinc and make them unavailable for absorption by the body. However, starchy foods such as potatoes, whole-grain cereals and wholemeal bread can be used as alternatives to bran – they are good sources of fibre that do not compromise the mineral status of older people. It is also important to top up fluid intake to enable the fibre to move easily through the gut. Drinking more water and eating water-rich foods such as vegetables and fruit can do this.

WHAT TO EAT

Older people must make sure that they are eating a variety of foods from the following four food groups each day:

- **Protein** Women need around 46g of protein each day, men need 63g. Get your quota by eating two to three portions of lean meat, fish, eggs, nuts, beans and lentils.
- **Dairy products** Calcium requirements can be met by consuming three or more servings of milk, cheese or yoghurt.
- **Fruits and vegetables** Try to eat five or more portions a day of fresh, frozen, canned or dried fruit or fruit juices.
- **Carbohydrates** Aim for five portions a day from bread, cereals, potatoes, pasta or rice.

Many factors affect food choices in old age, such as taste, convenience and price, as well as ease of preparation and ability to chew. The recipe below requires little preparation and is a good source of fibre, calcium and vitamins.

STEWED DRIED FRUIT WITH YOGHURT

40g dried apricots
40g prunes
40g dried figs
2 tsp runny honey
2 tsp lemon juice
1 cinnamon stick
1 clove
1 pot plain yoghurt

Mix the fruit in a bowl, add about 250ml of warm water to cover and leave to soak overnight. Transfer the fruit and liquid to a small saucepan, and add the honey, cinnamon stick, clove and lemon juice, then simmer the mixture for about 15 minutes or until the fruit is soft. Serve warm with yoghurt.
Serves 2

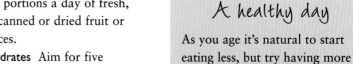

A healthy day

As you age it's natural to start eating less, but try having more frequent smaller meals with nutritious snacks in between. Here are suggestions for a healthy day's menu:

BREAKFAST
Porridge made with skimmed or semi-skimmed milk with a sliced banana
Glass of orange juice
Slice of wholemeal toast with reduced-fat spread

LUNCH
Wholemeal bread sandwich with ham, thinly sliced tomatoes and lettuce
Pot of fruit yoghurt
Slice of melon

DINNER
Fish pie made with cod, salmon, hard-boiled eggs and mashed potato, served with peas and carrots
Baked apple with raisins and custard

SNACKS
Wholemeal scone with reduced-fat spread
Bowl of home-made soup with wholemeal bread
Digestive biscuits with reduced-fat cheese
Fruit, such as orange segments, mango slices or grapes

A LIFETIME OF EXERCISE NEEDS

Junk foods and little or no exercise are turning children with the potential to stay fit and healthy into adults with all sorts of health problems, compromising what may be a good inheritance for the heart, bones and other body systems. Crucial to health in later life are harnessing children's natural exuberance and keeping them interested in exercise through the teen years and beyond. The best way to do this is to lead by example, with fitness a family activity in which everyone takes part and which everyone enjoys.

 68

We are increasingly suffering from problems that could be avoided by adequate exercise: getting children into exercise early pays dividends.

 73

It is easy for even a fit kid to turn couch potato teen but regular exercise is vital for future health and growth.

 74

Exercise should be regular and enjoyable so choose activities you like and a schedule that fits your lifestyle for best results.

Exercise for children

Exercise has many physical, psychological and social benefits for children. There are plenty of fun leisure activities they can choose from, which will dramatically improve fitness levels without feeling like hard work.

Keeping fit and healthy is important at any age. As we are now living longer, fuller lives it has become even more important. You can't stop yourself getting ill from disease or infection, but you can keep your body in as good a condition as possible. This means keeping both your body and mind alert and 'well oiled' – just as you would do with your car.

To keep the mind and body in good condition you simply have to put them to work on a regular basis. The mind tends to stay active because we work and constantly have to use it to solve problems. Yet sometimes the body can get overlooked, particularly for those whose jobs involve little or no physical activity. If we can stay active and thereby keep the muscles toned and bones strong, we can work out our very own protection system.

GET THE HABIT

Getting the habit of being active is important right from an early age: it's never too early to introduce an active routine. Get your baby out of the cot to explore the outside world. In a safe environment, letting your baby roll around and then toddle is great for both of you. Two and three-year-olds can benefit from racing around and playing active games such as races, swinging, climbing and supervised water play.

Children who exercise young tend to stay active throughout their lives with raised self-esteem as a result.

Remember too that less time is given in schools to sport and exercise. As schools are pressured for academic results there is a tendency to offer only the minimum amount of time for sports in favour of a more pressing revision session. Parents need to encourage their children to be physically active to fill this void.

Getting them involved in a local club will build up their bodies as well as their social network and help them learn to relax through activity. Whilst TV cannot be denied children all the time (and it is a powerful modern information tool), watching too much TV can leave a child with an over-stimulated brain and no physical outlet for it but frustrated behaviour. Monitor TV time so that it does not become the major part of your child's day.

TRY FAMILY FITNESS

Family fitness is taking on greater importance as parents realise that children learn by watching their example. Also, some parents who are pressed for time have figured out that if they combine their fitness efforts with their children's classes they save time. Why not go out for a quick jog while your child is in gymnastics class? Or attend a class at the fitness centre while your teenager has a tennis lesson? Try to plan some

active family outings: walking, visitng a public garden or organising a game of rounders or baseball are easy activities that help a family have fun and unwind together.

FITNESS FOR CHILDREN

Many people are aware of the growing problem of obesity in adults, and the same problem is emerging in children. At present it is estimated that a million British under-16s are obese. (Obese is the next size up from overweight; technically, it is more than 6.5 kilos

Family fun

When exercise is seen as a fun activity, it is a great way for both children and parents to get fit and to enjoy the many health benefits of regular exercise in the fresh air.

IS YOUR CHILD GETTING ENOUGH EXERCISE?

Try our simple quiz to get a basic indication of whether your child is getting enough physical activity to promote good health.

My child spends:
a) more than four hours a day watching television
b) one to four hours a day watching television
c) less than one hour a day watching television

My child takes part in:
a) an occasional game of football, rounders or other sport
b) more than one sport or activity throughout the year
c) several sports or activities throughout the year

Our family plans:
a) an outdoor activity such as walking, biking, roller skating or outdoor games once a year
b) an outdoor activity each month
c) an outdoor activity each week

My children walk to school, the park and around the neighbourhood:
a) rarely
b) two to three times per week
c) everyday

At present, my child would most enjoy playing:
a) a video game
b) a board game
c) on a bike or skateboard

Activities I enjoy most with my child are:
a) watching our favourite TV programme
b) walking or playing outdoors
c) taking a long ride, walk or playing races

My child is used to seeing my partner or me:
a) exercising once a year
b) exercising once a month
c) exercising once a week

For each A answer count 1 point, for each B answer 2 points and each C answer 3 points.

6–8 points. Your child could do with more exercise but don't panic. You simply need to implement a few small adjustments to your child's schedule. Read on to find out how to make subtle changes that will make a big difference.

9–14 points. Your child is getting some exercise but adding a few more activities would boost fitness levels. Read on for more ideas.

15–18 points. Your child is probably getting enough exercise. Keep up the good work.

– a stone – over the ideal weight for a person's height.) The story is similar in other countries too. More and more young people are signing on to the books of personal trainers as their parents become concerned about their children's weight gain. A chief scientist for Weight Watchers has remarked: 'Obesity among children is increasing at an alarming rate and the health consequences are very severe.' All the health problems that overweight adults get can happen with children too. For example, type II diabetes is also known as late-onset diabetes as it typically emerged in adults in their 40s or later, but today it increasingly affects people in their 20s or even in their teens.

WHAT IS THE PROBLEM?

The root cause of the weight problem is the same as it is for adults – not enough exercise and too much food. Melinda Southern, PhD, Director of the Childhood Obesity laboratory at Louisiana State University has commented, 'It's no coincidence that the same two decades that brought us soaring obesity rates also brought us cable TV, home computers ... fast food restaurants and the verb *super-size*.' Childhood stories of our grandparents' generation usually involve heading across the fields to play all day, catching fish by the riverbank. Even classic children's stories from earlier eras talk of children camping and playing in the fields or woodland.

Today, however, parents are much more worried about letting their children out of doors unsupervised and fitness and activity levels have fallen accordingly.

1a

1b

A CHILD-FRIENDLY WORKOUT

Why not try exercising with your child? The exercises here can get the whole family moving. If you don't have time on mormal weekdays, try to make time at weekends and during holidays.

1 Stretch up
Stretch your hands up over your head and lift up on your toes as high as you can. Now bend your knees and curl into a tight ball, rounding your back and tucking your head in. Do this five times.

2 Jog on the spot
Jog where you are standing for two minutes. Keep chatting to each other the whole time. You could test your kids times tables or spellings as you jog.

3 Squat downs
Stand with your hands on your hips, bend your knees and sit on your heels (heels are off the ground). Push yourself back up again. Do this five times.

4 Twister sister
Stand with your feet wide apart and swing your arms round behind you, keeping your knees and hips facing the front. Swing your arms back the other way. Swing your arms eight times each way. Make sure you are far enough away from walls and furniture so you don't hit anything.

5 Partner arches
Stand opposite your partner (brother, sister, mum or dad) and hold hands. Now gently arch your back slightly and then pull yourself back to upright. Do this three times.

2

3a

3b

4a

4b

5a

5b

Self-defence for self-esteem
Sports such as karate and judo offer children social interaction and encourage self-confidence; they also improve coordination.

WHAT CAN PARENTS DO?

As parents you can lead by example and give lots of encouragement. Be guided by your child's preferences – don't push your child too hard into an activity he or she may not feel ready for. If your child refuses your offer of tennis lessons, wait six months then offer again. If your child wants to swim, then go along and offer encouragement. Focus on your child's successes rather than refusals or failures. If children enjoy an activity, they are more likely to stick at it.

EXERCISE FOR CHILDREN UNDER SIX

It can be difficult to gauge what is appropriate for young children. Some parents may be concerned about the nature of the exercise their child is doing, too. Generally, most experts recommend leaving out team sports and games until the child is over seven because most team games are contact sports and can be rough. Some suggestions for pre-team sports are karate, judo, gymnastics, swimming, dancing, hopscotch, rounders, tennis, and organised fitness training to build up for team sports such as football or hockey.

EXERCISE FOR THE OVER-SEVENS

Children over seven can start to expand their range of activities. This is the age at which children start to show a preference towards one kind of sport over another. Some good activities include skating, bicycle riding, hockey, lacrosse, easy hiking, gymnastics, tennis and football. Distance running is usually best postponed until adolescence.

STRENGTH TRAINING FOR KIDS

Many parents become concerned that strength training is not appropriate for a growing child or teenager. Strength training needs to be explained. There is often confusion between the terms 'strength training' and 'weight lifting'. Weight lifting or bodybuilding is a separate sport in which the participants are competing to lift the heaviest weight they possibly can. Bodybuilders lift huge weights and develop large, bulky muscles. Strength training is very different. It is not about how heavy a weight you can lift, but strengthening the whole musculoskeletal system which can be as beneficial for a child as it is for an adult.

Power lifting, weight lifting and bodybuilding are not recommended for children, but several studies have shown strength training – working the muscles against resistance – to be effective and it is now endorsed by sports bodies. It is a way to improve fitness levels and build strength and coordination in children providing the programme is well devised and properly supervised.

Children as young as five and six can do abdominal exercises or push-ups, developing coordination and agility in the process. Seven and eight-year-olds can use weights as long as they are supervised and are capable of concentrating enough to follow the regime. Make sure your child sees strength training in perspective, as a means to an end that will improve fitness, timing, running and scoring skills.

SAFETY

Getting children into fitness is a great idea but make sure you do your best to prevent accidents.

- When biking, scooting or skateboarding children should wear a helmet and appropriate protective gear.
- Make sure children have a safe area in which to exercise without having to cross roads without you.
- Don't leave children under 11 alone around a pool and keep safety floats handy.
- To prevent sun damage, teach your child to apply sunscreen before going out and to wear a hat in the sun.

Exercise and teenagers

Recent research has shown that, contrary to popular belief, teenagers want to spend more time exercising. Aware of their sedentary lifestyles spent watching TV, most want to become more active, and surprisingly want to do so with their parents.

Teenagers, like children, benefit from regular exercise. While your teenager may be at a stage where you feel they don't listen to a word you say, you are still a role model. Sometimes actions speak louder than words, so show by example.

WHAT PARENTS CAN DO

Although teenagers like to assume autonomy they still need guidance. When you can, make time to watch your teenagers if they participate in sports and congratulate them on any achievements. Encourage them to be fit and healthy but don't focus on how much they weigh. If your teen is overweight you need to approach the matter carefully and sensitively.

What to do if your teenager is overweight

- Suggest occasional family activities. Teenagers may not join in all the time but it will register in their subconscious.
- Suggest new clubs or activities to try.
- Offer healthy foods and get teenagers involved in the food shopping. Keep the foods on the plate colourful, using spinach, squash, peppers and carrots. A variety of colours are usually a sign of a variety of nutrients.
- Get rid of the bathroom scales. Focus on fitness rather than weight. Steer away from diets but emphasise healthy foods.

- If you think your teenager really has a weight problem you could enlist the services of a nutritionist or personal trainer who can set out some specific fitness goals: for example, to be able to run faster or jump higher, rather than focusing on weight loss.

What type of exercise?

Teenagers can try almost any kind of exercise that takes their fancy, but bodybuilding and weight-lifting are still not recommended. They should aim to include activities that cover the three basic tenets of fitness.

- Cardiovascular exercise to build up stamina, such as running, soccer or aerobics.
- Exercises to enhance flexibility, such as gymnastics, dance or martial arts.
- Exercises to build up endurance such as strength training, skiing or swimming.

6 Benefits of exercise for a teenager

Regular exercise not only builds fitness but can have a real impact on how teenagers feel about themselves, improving confidence and self-esteem.

1 Teenagers spend much of their time occupied with school work and exams. Physical exercise is one of the best ways to unwind and it also stimulates the brain's ability to learn.

2 Studies show that active teenagers tend to feel less lonely and shy, have fewer feelings of hopelessness and have greater self-esteem than their less active counterparts.

3 Adherence to a regular training programme or sport training session can teach adherence to other schedules, such as revision or essay plans.

4 Exercise uses up time and energy. This leaves less time for teenagers to become bored and dissatisfied. If teenagers are keen to build physical prowess and fitness, they may be less tempted to try drugs and alcohol.

5 Aerobic exercise appears to have a positive effect on behaviour, stress and anxiety. Physical activity releases endorphins, which contribute to feelings of well-being. At a time of hormonal mood swings, the more endorphins the better.

6 Exercise is an excellent channel for letting off steam and has been shown to make improvements in aggressive behaviour.

Keeping fit and healthy

Most of us live in a hectic round of daily activity, embracing speed, convenience and time-saving tactics. It is important, however, to schedule regular time out for exercise in order to reap the benefits later in life.

BENEFITS FOR ADULTS

Many benefits of exercise are more specific to adults.

- Activity pulls on bones and muscles and slows down adult bone loss that begins after the age of 25–30, helping to prevent osteoporosis.
- De-stressing and relaxation are important benefits of exercise for adults. As our lives get more complicated with more and more technology and greater demands on our time, taking time out to relax our brains and exercise our bodies is a great all-round mental health booster.
- Weight control is an issue for many adults. Regular active pursuits and exercise or sports sessions can really help to ensure that as the years pile up, the fat doesn't.
- Apart from keeping the heart and bones healthy, exercise is great for keeping you moving and socialising. As we get older our lives tend to become more insular with fewer opportunities for

socialising than when we were young. Exercise gets us out and about meeting new people.

- Raising energy and mood levels is an important issue for adults. Regular activity can improve heart and lung function and encourage the release of endorphins, which improves mood.

There is growing evidence, too, that exercise and a healthy lifestyle can help slow down the onset of some major diseases. Type II diabetes can be radically helped with diet and exercise and many types of heart problem benefit too. The World Cancer Research Fund also states: 'One in three of us is likely to be affected by cancer at some stage…'. The good news is that '… it is largely a preventable disease.' World Cancer Research has examined over 4,500 studies on the links between diet, lifestyle and cancer. As a result they were able to devise

six diet and health guidelines for cancer prevention, one of which is to stay physically active.

Overcoming problems and excuses

Only one in three adults exercise regularly and many who do exercise are not considered to be doing enough. For some adults, staying physically active may not be an easy thing to do. Some of these problems are of our own making, but others are out of our control.

As we get older, even in our twenties and thirties, our lifestyle tends to make us less active. Many adults travel everywhere by car or other transport; meetings are conducted sitting down; evenings are largely spent sitting and chatting or watching some kind of entertainment. Unless we make specific plans, natural exercise is greatly reduced once we own a car and have a sedentary job.

The solution, of course, is to make a conscious effort to fit in some activity time. This does not have to be official 'exercise'. Try walking short journeys instead of driving. Put your back into cleaning the house vigorously, reaching high and low to fit in some natural exercise. Or clean the car by hand rather than using a car wash.

Feel good fresh air
Regular exercise, particularly done outdoors, boosts the immune system and helps to release stress, tension and fatigue.

One consistent problem for adults is time, or rather the lack of it. With a job, a house to run and possibly children to look after too, making time for exercise can seem very low on the agenda. It is vital to prioritise exercise time. Make an entry in your diary, as you would for a meeting or an appointment with your GP. Schedule things around it so that you fit it in. Get up early to fit a little exercise regime in – it doesn't have to be more than 10 minutes, yet 10 minutes done consistently three times a week can really build up some health benefits. It is much more worthwhile than an extra 10 minutes in bed.

Variety can also be a problem for adults. We get more easily bored as we grow older, feeling we have seen and done it all before. Setting goals is one of the keys to keeping motivated. Consult a personal trainer or gym instructor who may be able to point out ways you can vary any programme you already have and move you onto the next stage. Look out for new ways of training or new ideas on exercises you can try.

Many adults can get into a downward spiral when it comes to looking after themselves. When the pressure is on, parents tend to put themselves last in line behind the demands of children and running a household. Workers put themselves on the line for their job. Under unrelenting pressure, it is small wonder that some people start to rely on alcohol, smoking, drugs and bad eating habits to escape the stress.

Sometimes it only takes one small incident to stop a bad habit and start a good one. A new fitness routine, a visit to a nutritionist to re-focus your eating habits or even just a day off for you to re-think and de-stress can help to get problems and tight schedules into proportion. Even making a small change can give you a sense of control over your life and will improve your self-esteem and motivation to look after yourself.

What adults should do
• Try to incorporate some form of general sport into your monthly regime. It is sociable, fun and will give your muscles a good workout.

Recording your workouts
By keeping a record of your exercise sessions each month, you will be more likely to achieve your fitness goals.

• Try to develop some kind of home routine you can do so that you can work a little each week on keeping up your energy levels.
• Try to incorporate some muscle-building work, some endurance work and some flexibility work into your routine.

MY WORKOUT LOG
Name: Emma Taylor
Month: August

	Goals for the week		Goals accomplished
Days of CV work	2	yes/no	yes
Days of weight training	1	yes/no	yes
Days of cross training	1	yes/no	no

Total exercise

MON	TUES	WED	THUR	FRI	SAT	SUN
					1	2
3 A 15(8)	4	5 W (8)	6	7 R 20(7)	8	9 C 20(8)
10	11 A 20(7)	12	13 W (10)	14	15 R 20(10)	16
17 A 10(10)	18	19 W (5)	20	21 R 20(5)	22	23 C 20(7)
24	25 R 15(8)	26	27 W (8)	28	29 A 20(5)	30
31						

Key: A=Aerobics, R=Run, W=Weights, C=Cross training
1–20=number of minutes
Intensity 1–10 (10=very hard)

FITNESS FOR THE ELDERLY

Fitness for the elderly is essentially the same as for all other ages. It benefits the body and the mind and the more regularly you do it the better you will feel.

Many studies point to the fact that quality of life for the older age group is closely related to physical fitness. Far too many people assume that old age means slowing down and the onset of inexorable limitations. While your lifestyle may lack the urgency of your middle years, your physical activities need not. It is never too late to start getting fit either, and the older you are the more you need to do it.

Don't jump to conclusions

As we age the body's systems do get worn. Injuries can take longer to heal and conditioning happens at a slower rate than in younger people. Periods of enforced bed rest (which

Gently does it
If taking up exercise for the first time, or after a long gap, it is essential to start slowly. Walking is an ideal form of light exercise to get the muscles going.

are more common in the elderly) certainly don't help fitness, but these disadvantages can be overcome with regular physical activity.

You should not assume, or accept, that getting fatter, stiffer or weaker or having difficulty lifting a shopping bag or getting up out of a chair, is a natural consequence of ageing. It is, however, natural if people do not exercise – and this can have dangerous consequences.

Frailty is a big risk to the ageing population. By the age of 70 most people have 20 per cent less muscle than they did at the age of 30. Some of this muscle deterioration is due to the ageing process, yet over half is caused by people becoming more sedentary with age. Studies show too, that heredity only accounts for 15 per cent of degeneration: the rest is habit.

Get out and enjoy yourself

The best thing you can do is to get out and do something. Experts say working out combats the frailty of old age and increases confidence and enjoyment of life. Many (though not all) of the niggles and gripes in our bodies can be overcome with exercise and thus it can help all but the most severely disabled. Elderly people can experience the excitement and boost in confidence that comes with the feeling of making gains in fitness just as the young do. While this will not guarantee a longer life, it will certainly improve quality of life.

Age-specific benefits

As you tone muscles and bones, you will be improving your flexibility and mobility and building muscle tone. Enhanced muscle tone and the improved balance that comes with it will strengthen bones and lessen the likelihood of falls, protecting bones from breakage and muscles from tearing. Regular activity can help the elderly to sleep better and thus recover from illness more quickly. Mental well-being will in turn be enhanced by better sleep. You may also find it easier to control your weight, and your blood pressure will be less inclined to creep up.

SUGGESTED EXERCISES FOR THE OLDER PERSON

As we get older our interests change and what is fun for us changes, so it is important to find something you enjoy doing and that feels right for you. Choose something that gives you pleasure and perhaps offers a social outlet too.

- **Dancing** A great fitness activity, age is no barrier to many fun dance classes, such as line dancing, ceroc, barn dances and ballroom.
- **Bowling** A social sport, it will keep your flexibility going as you bend and roll.
- **Fitness classes** These are available at both health clubs and local authority gyms. You can try out anything from fit ball to Pilates. Yoga, for example, will strengthen and tone you and give you a feeling of well-being.
- **Walking** You could join a ramblers group or just meet with friends for weekly treks.
- **Tennis or badminton** These allow you to meet new people. You could join a local club while you learn.

- Tai chi A non-contact martial art, this will challenge and calm you, improve your ability to focus and concentrate, and improve your balance and muscle tone.
- Swimming A great sport for all ages, it tones all the major muscles of the body and gives you a good aerobic workout. Because the water sustains your weight, swimming doesn't stress your joints.

HOW TO GET STARTED

By the time you get to 65 or 70 you should be familiar with the concept of exercise. However, we all have periods when we get out of shape and out of the habit of regular activity. If you are thinking of returning to exercise or planning to start some new activity follow these basic guidelines.

Start slowly and build up gradually

If you participated in a sport at a younger age you may think you can get your previous form back quickly. Take your time and you will avoid injuries due to over-enthusiasm. If you are starting something new remember that muscle and muscle-brain pathways take time to establish so don't be impatient with yourself. If you do a little every few days you will soon see an improvement.

Don't hesitate to seek advice

Speak to your doctor for reassurance that you are ready to exercise. If you need advice on a new kind of exercise or activity then ask at the gym, consult a personal trainer (who are more reasonably priced these days) or buy a book. There are some very good books and videos on the market, which can give sound pointers and help to keep you safe as you build up your exercise regime.

WARM UP AND COOL DOWN

Warming up is literally lubricating your system in readiness for exercise. Cooling down allows your heart rate and muscles to return to normal after you have exerted yourself. Before and after exercise, try marching on the spot for 5–10 minutes, swinging your arms and legs, and do some basic stretches.

MUSCLE RELAXATION

Once you have adopted a regular fitness regime it is also important to learn how to relax properly.

- First, find a comfortable place where you will be left alone. If necessary, unplug the telephone.
- Lie on the floor on your back, or sit in a comfortable chair, and close your eyes.
- Breathe in and out, focusing on each breath. Relax your shoulders.
- Lengthen the breaths so that you can count up to five for each in-breath and each out-breath.
- Picture a warm, beautiful, peaceful place in your mind's eye.
- Now focus on your body. Squeeze your toes, count to three and then release the contraction. Next, squeeze your calf muscles, count to three and then relax them.
- Repeat this for each part of the body, down your arms to your fingers. Work your way up to your head, finishing with your forehead.

Grace and poise
Research has shown that older people who participate in t'ai chi gain strength and improve their balance. This helps them to avoid frailty and decreases the risk of falling.

LOOKING AND FEELING GOOD

Research suggests that even children experience stress today – indeed, few life stages and events are stress-free. Attitude can make the difference between stress that is harmful to emotional well-being and stress that energises. It helps to understand the potential threats to mental health at different life stages, and to act promptly to deal with problems.

79

There is a genetic component to mental health, but having a good support network can help you to handle stress and keep on an even keel.

81

Making the most of what nature has given you can help you to feel in control of your life – a major factor in staying mentally healthy.

84

Although the amount of sleep we need changes through life, a regular sleep pattern and quality sleep remain essential to health.

Good mental health

In Britain one in three people will experience mental illness during their life; this can include anxiety, depression, phobias, obsession or schizophrenia. There is now a wide range of support available for people with a mental health problem.

Our mental health is a product of nature and nurture – of our genetic endowment, our upbringing and the world in which we find ourselves. Good mental health could be defined as the psychological capacity to experience life to its fullest. This includes the capacity to grow, to face new challenges with conviction, be open to change and to learn from any situation.

Personality has been judged to be about 50–60 per cent attributable to inheritance, a conclusion based largely on studies of identical twins. Personality traits are important in determining how an individual copes with day-to-day stressors that could upset their mental balance.

MENTAL HEALTH AND GENETIC INHERITANCE

Most people with mental illness do not come from a family with a history of the illness. Although schizophrenia and bipolar depression are largely thought of as being hereditary, it is more accurate to say that one can inherit a predisposition or increased vulnerability to the illness. Having a family history of a mental illness does not mean you will necessarily get the illness, but you may have an increased risk.

An increased risk is only one of several factors that contribute to the development of the illness. It is likely that mental disorders involve a chemical imbalance and are triggered by stressful life events, drug abuse or hormonal changes.

Anxiety

More than one in ten people suffer from some form of anxiety disorder. Researchers have now found that anxiety may in part be an inherited condition linked to a specific gene – the SLC6A4 gene – which affects the transmission of serotonin within the brain. Each parent passes either a short or a long version of the gene to their offspring. The short version transports serotonin less efficiently and people with one or two of these genes tend to show abnormal levels of anxiety.

Depression

Mild depression appears to run in families, and is believed to be caused by genetic factors which are then triggered by environmental factors. In their lifetime, about one per cent of people with depression develop bipolar disorder (previously known as manic depression). If a person has relatives with bipolar disorder then their risk is higher. About 12 per cent of people with a sibling with bipolar disorder will develop the condition themselves.

LIVING WITH A MENTAL HEALTH PROBLEM

With proper care and treatment many individuals learn to cope or recover from a mental illness or emotional disorder. Although a mental illness can affect an individual's daily life, there are many things that can help towards coping more effectively.

- **Seek information** Although there are few certain answers about mental illness, there are broad guidelines which can help.
- **Broaden the support network** Friends, neighbours, colleagues and self-help groups can often give practical assistance.
- **Learn to spot warning signs** Try to assess the emotions, behaviour and attitudes that precede problem.
- **Don't expect too much of yourself** – and don't blame yourself.
- **Talk about the situation** If you need further help or support contact a self-help group or counsellor.
- **Don't give up too soon** Recovery from a mental illness takes time and cannot be rushed.

There is a history of clinical depression in my family. Should I have children?

There is a statistical correlation between a family history of clinical depression and an increased risk of an individual and their children developing depression. However, this risk should not be overstated and should not be a reason for stigma. An awareness of the risk, appropriate vigilance and preventative strategies may mean depression does not occur, and early effective treatment improves the prognosis if it does occur. A risk of depression alone should not be a reason not to have children. The details and specific strategies should be discussed with your GP.

ASK THE EXPERT

MANAGING STRESS

One of the keys to good mental health is knowing how to deal with stress. No-one can avoid stress completely – it is a natural reaction to everyday challenges and changes. Even positive experiences, like having a baby or getting a promotion, can cause stress.

In many cases, the greatest threat is not from the stress in itself, but from how the person reacts to it. People need the skills to resist or adapt to stress before it leaves them feeling out of control and takes a toll on their health. Although not the primary cause, stress can be a factor in health problems such as infections, migraines, allergies, ulcers, high blood pressure and heart disease. The following are effective stress-busting methods that can help you to cope with the strains of everyday life.

- Learn how to relax.
- Plan breaks in your day and split your workload into manageable chunks.
- Adopt an optimistic attitude.
- Talk to friends, family or colleagues about worries.
- Exercise regularly.
- Don't leave it too long before taking a short break or holiday.

THINKING POSITIVELY

A positive and open attitude to life can dramatically affect the way you feel: it can help you to avoid getting stuck in your ways or living in the past, it can enhance receptivity to new ideas, and help keep problems and worries in proportion. There are a number of areas that can be addressed to help the average person achieve optimal mental health:

- **Avoiding 'shoulds'** Often people find that in trying to motivate themselves they develop a list of 'shoulds', such as 'I should have studied more' or 'I shouldn't have eaten so much'. This can be a way of punishing yourself and is extremely draining. Try to be more realistic about your personal goals.
- **The relentless critic** Do you seem to find fault with everything? Do you constantly nag other people? Try replacing criticism with encouragement or compliments. Visualise the positive in situations and offer support to other people.
- **Perfectionism** If you believe that you must do everything perfectly or not at all, it may be time to relax. Just do your best and then accept it. You could seek help if your perfectionist tendencies are holding you back.

- **Negative interpretation** Often people choose only to see the downside of a situation. This can be very wearing to be around. Try looking at things positively. If someone compliments you, don't think there's a hidden catch. Accept the compliment and feel good!

FRIENDSHIP

Research shows that friends are beneficial for our psychological well-being. Friends help us to cope with stress. They also make us feel cared for and loved. This feeling of worthiness helps us to think in a positive way about stressful events and is invaluable for maintaining good mental health. For people looking to develop their circle of friends, a good starting point would be to join a special interest group to meet like-minded people.

Friendship is good for health
A strong social network is linked to good mental health, as well as lower mortality rates for both healthy and unhealthy people.

Maximising your potential

Although the process of ageing is inevitable, 'feeling old' isn't. Men and women who enjoy an active, fulfilling old age usually have something in common: a positive attitude to life. Try to look forwards and make the most of what you've got.

LIVING LONGER

Life expectancy in the 20th century increased by approximately 20 years in the UK, to 81 years for women and 74 for men. This is good news provided we stay in shape and there is a lot we can do to ensure that we stay healthy for this longer life.

Genetics plays a part in determining how long we live. If your parents were long-lived, that increases the chances that you will be too. However, genetics account for only 25 per cent of our longevity and health. The rest is down to lifestyle factors, such as environment and nutrition, so a great deal of it is in our own hands. Statistics show that those who are economically better off are more likely to live longer and stay healthier, but healthy lifestyle choices do not have to cost more money than unhealthy ones.

HEALTHY HABITS

It is important to keep unhealthy lifestyle habits to a minimum from an early age, to lessen the impact of these habits later in life – moderation is the key. Health experts agree that there are crucial things we can do to prolong our span of good health by lessening damage to cells and tissues and enhancing the body's ability to repair itself. These include:

• Taking at least 15 minutes of vigorous exercise at least three times a week.
• Eating a healthy diet low in fat and salt, with at least five portions of fruit and vegetables each day.
• Not smoking.
• Consuming alcohol in moderation.
• Maintaining a healthy weight.

LOOKING YOUNGER

A healthy lifestyle can make us look and feel generally younger than our chronological age. However, even if we follow a healthy lifestyle, there are days when we wake up feeling under the weather, then look in the mirror to find that our appearance matches the way we feel. Perhaps the skin looks dry and parched, eyes puffy and shadowed, hair lank.

If this happens to you and you're not actually ill, the answer is probably to do with how well you slept, or the fact that you forgot your night-time moisturiser, or didn't have a glass of water before going to bed. A few simple steps can help to restore a more radiant glow:

• **Drink up** Often fluid retention is to blame for a puffy face. If the body becomes dehydrated it tries to hold onto all the water it can and as a result blood vessels enlarge and the face swells up. Have a glass of water as soon as you wake up. Avoid coffee or tea in the morning as this could make it worse.
• **Massage** Puffiness can be due to poor circulation. Stroke your fingertips around the eye sockets and then across the eyebrows; try pulling faces to stretch the muscles.
• **Moisturise** For good-looking skin, both men and women should apply moisturiser before bed, as it is absorbed better at this time. A cream or lotion which contains the antioxidant vitamins A, C and E will help to protect against the damage caused by free radicals.

AGEING WITH ATTITUDE

Everyone knows the saying 'you're as young as you feel', and there seems to be some truth in it. Becoming more sedentary, for example, is a frequent sign of getting older, but it is not compulsory and will almost certainly have an adverse affect on health. In contrast, if you keep physically active this will help to keep your body's systems in good shape, and keep you looking and feeling younger than an inactive person of the same age. Similarly, stimulating your mental faculties helps to preserve them as well as making you feel stimulated and alive.

Approaching senior years is often seen as a series of losses – the loss of work, status, physical prowess – and it's often held that depression is more prevalent in older age groups. Recent research has shown the opposite may be true, however, and that ageing can give people a new lease of life. *The Jubilee Report,* published in the UK in 2002, found that most women questioned were more fulfilled, more independent and enjoyed better relationships than ever before.

In a survey published in 2002, 65 per cent of women reported that they felt happier, healthier and had better sex lives after the onset of the menopause.

WORKING WITHIN YOUR GENETIC FRAMEWORK

Exercise will almost certainly improve a person's appearance, but intrinsic body shape is to a large extent a matter of heredity. Everyone is born with a basic body type, as defined by fat distribution, fat-to-muscle ratio, limb length and body shape. There are three classic types:

- **Endomorph** A round, soft, pear-shaped body supported by small bones. The legs, arms and neck are short and heavy, the hips are broad and the shoulders narrow.
- **Mesomorph** A rectangular outline with large bones, broad shoulders and long neck. They build muscle easily and look athletic.
- **Ectomorph** A slender, sometimes frail looking body, due to small bones, long arms and legs, a short trunk and small hips.

Most people are a blend of these three types, but resemble one type more than the others. Exercise cannot change a person from one type to another, but will enhance the potential of each body type.

Once you understand your body type, you can set reasonable fitness goals and avoid the stress and disappointment of unrealistic expectations. Women often strive unsuccessfully to achieve a certain body image without any thought to their genetic make up. Likewise, inherited body type will affect how a person builds up muscles through exercise. Heredity dictates the ratio of slow-twitch and fast-twitch fibres that form muscles. Slow-twitch fibres are used for endurance activities. Fast-twitch fibres are powerful and can be built up by weight-training.

Weight

Whatever genes you've inherited, unhealthy eating and insufficient exercise will cause you to put on weight. However, some people do have a genetic predisposition to excess weight. The recommended average for body fat is 22 per cent but this may not be achievable by everyone. A woman who is already below 30 per cent, follows a low-fat diet and exercises for a year, and still

doesn't get down to 22 per cent, may have to accept a predisposition to higher body fat. One way to change unrealistic weight goals is simply to aim for the weight you feel best at – one where you have plenty of energy and which you can maintain. Women especially should accept a range that allows for natural weight fluctuations.

Metabolism

If you consume more calories than you burn off, you will gain weight. However, some people metabolise food differently and burn calories at a different rate. People with a rapid metabolism can sometimes handle higher levels of carbohydrates than those with a slow metabolism. Metabolism rates are hereditary, but exercise can help to speed up a slow metabolism: as the demand for energy increases the speed at which calories are burned also increases.

Going the distance
Champion marathon runners are often lean and slender, but a person of any body type can run for fun, as in the London Marathon.

Simple style

The best way to look good is to keep it simple, no long detailed routines, but a few simple habits that you will stick to.

1 Skin care
Get yourself into the routine of thorough facial cleansing morning and night, which will combat a large proportion of skin problems. Apply a moisturiser with a UV filter in the morning to avoid any extra skin damage by the sun and make sure that if you wear make-up you also remove it again before you go to sleep. If you enjoy it, treat yourself to a professional facial from time to time.

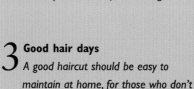

2 Posture
A lot of back problems are caused by bad posture and when your back aches it is easier to slouch which seems to give some short-term relief. But it will not do any good in the long-term. Stand up straight with your shoulders back. You will instantly look taller and slimmer. If you can get yourself into this good habit (try to mimic this also when you sit down) you may avoid back problems or find existing ones ease.

5 Watch what you eat
Small adjustments to your diet can achieve some excellent results. Switch to low-fat products and cut out sugary drinks, cakes, biscuits and salted snacks to feel better without 'dieting'. Look after your teeth with regular cleaning and dental check-ups.

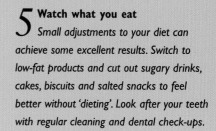

3 Good hair days
A good haircut should be easy to maintain at home, for those who don't have the time or inclination for hairdryers, curling tongs or styling products. Opt for a style that does not need loads of fiddling when you get up in the morning. If you get bored with it but can't afford a trip to the salon, there are lots of 'wash-in/wash-out' colours to give hair a boost.

4 Clothing to suit
Instead of trying to fit into a size or style just because it happens to be in fashion, look for clothing that suits you. Get basics that fit you properly, in colours that will go well together. For both men and women a basic well-fitting wardrobe will provide staple items to build on with different coloured tops and accessories. Buy shoes that are comfortable for everyday wear. This will help to eliminate backache and sore feet.

Sleep needs for optimum health

A rejuvenating night's sleep is essential for maintaining good health, but frequent late nights and stress can jeopardise sleep quality. Our sleep needs decrease as we age, and there are plenty of techniques to encourage more efficient sleep.

WHY SLEEP IS NECESSARY

Sleep is essential for survival. This has been proven in scientific experiments with rats. Rats normally live for two to three years, but if they are deprived of REM (rapid eye movement) sleep they live for barely more than a month; rats deprived of all sleep live for only three weeks. Further, sleep deprivation causes rats to have very low body temperatures. They also develop sores on their paws and tail, probably because sleep deprivation adversely affects their immune system.

Sleep enables our nervous systems to work properly, while insufficient sleep causes drowsiness and impaired concentration, and also leads to impaired memory and physical performance. Mental functions, such as mathematical calculations, are poor. If there is too little sleep for too long, mood swings and hallucinations may develop. Sleep allows neurons, which we use while we are awake, a chance to shut down and repair themselves. Lack of sleep causes the neurons to become depleted in energy or so polluted with by-products of normal cellular activities that they malfunction. Sleep also gives the brain a chance to exercise neuronal connections that would otherwise deteriorate from lack of use.

WHAT TAKES PLACE DURING DEEP SLEEP?

In children and young adults, growth hormone is released during deep sleep. There is also an increased production and reduced breakdown of proteins in many cells of the body, which is why deep sleep is often referred to as 'beauty sleep'. Such proteins are the building blocks for cell growth and repair the damage from stress, ultraviolet rays, cigarette smoke and other factors. Deep sleep is also important for optimal social and emotional functioning during wakefulness, because during deep sleep there is a decrease in the brain activities that control emotions, social interactions and decision-making. Finally, research in rats has shown that some nerve-signalling patterns generated during the day are repeated during deep sleep. This repetition may help to encode memories and improve learning.

HOW MUCH SLEEP IS NORMAL?

The average amount of sleep needed by adults is between seven and eight hours a night. However, some people need more than nine hours sleep each night while others do very well on less than six. But it isn't simply how many hours that you sleep each night that counts. What matters is how good you feel and how well you're able to perform each day.

Recent research has found an underlying biological reason for the differences in sleep requirements for

Proper sleep support
Check that you have a quality mattress and pillow: it's hard to sleep well in a lumpy or uncomfortable bed. Special pillows or boards are useful for neck and back problems.

individuals. Scientists studied a group of both long-sleepers and short-sleepers in a sleep laboratory, measuring their hormone levels, body temperature and other physiological markers. This pointed to the length of the circadian cycle, which is the internal clock that controls our sleep and wake cycles. What they found was that long-sleepers had a longer biological sleep time than short-sleepers did. So it is biology that drives the need for a longer night's sleep and not, as is often assumed, habit or laziness. Sleepers who wake early have been found to have higher levels of the stress hormone cortisol.

Other scientists have discovered a new light-sensitive pigment in the eye, the skin and part of the brain responsible for the body's internal clock. Their research could lead to better remedies for jet lag, as well as ways to improve working conditions for those on night shift.

GETTING A GOOD NIGHT'S SLEEP

There are many possible causes for insomnia including breathing problems, heart disease, sleep apnoea, depression, anxiety, excessive worrying, too much caffeine or alcohol, disruption of the sleep/wake cycle because of shift work, or poor sleep hygiene. However, there are ways to improve your chances of getting a good night's sleep. To sleep well:
• Make sure your bedroom is peaceful and quiet. If there is traffic or other outside noise try listening to relaxing music on a radio or CD player with a timer that will switch itself off after you are likely to have fallen asleep.

An alternative is to buy a machine that creates 'white noise'. This may take a while to get used to, but it works by drowning out other noise so that you fall asleep undisturbed.
• Make sure that your bedroom is dark enough. If you prefer the comfort of a little light in the bedroom have a night-light or small lamp.
• Buy a comfortable mattress and pillows. A mattress that is too hard or too soft will make it difficult for you to relax well.
• Exercise regularly, but not too close to bedtime.
• A glass of milk, warm or cold, before you go to bed will probably soothe you. Avoid alcohol and stimulants, especially caffeine, which is found in most coffee, cola drinks and chocolate. Consume caffeine only during the day or early evening and at least several hours before you go to bed.
• To counteract worry or stress, relax with a book or magazine. Choose one that is interesting enough to make you to want to read it, but not so exciting that it over-stimulates you.
• If you wake in the night and can't get back to sleep within 15 minutes, switch on the light and read or listen to relaxing music until you fall asleep again.
• Get up at the same time every day regardless of your bedtime.

A BABY'S SLEEP NEEDS

Babies need a lot of sleep. In fact, a newborn baby sleeps most of the time. But as babies get older, they gradually stop napping and start doing all of their sleeping at night. Children in nursery and infant school need 10 or 11 hours of sleep a night,

Why should babies sleep on their backs?

By putting your baby on his or her back to sleep, even for naps, you reduce the risk of SIDS (sudden infant death syndrome). This is contrary to the advice that used to be given to parents until a few years ago. Avoid putting your baby in the side position because from there babies can easily roll onto their stomach. Sometimes parents worry about the risk of their baby choking on its back, but in fact there is no risk because babies automatically swallow or cough up fluids.

ASK THE EXPERT

but that will gradually decrease. By the early teenage years they will need only 9–10 hours of sleep per night.

Quiet sleep and active sleep
The sleep of a newborn baby is divided into quiet sleep and active sleep, the two states alternating about every 30 minutes. In quiet sleep, the baby's face is relaxed and the eyelids are closed and still. There are no body movements except for very occasional startles and extremely tiny mouth movements. They are fully at rest and their breathing is very regular. In active sleep their eyes are usually closed, but occasionally they will flutter from closed to open. The eyes move under the eyelids: this is rapid eye movement (REM) sleep. In this sleep activity may range from occasional movement of the arms and legs to movement of the entire body.

Average sleep needs through life

Our sleep needs change throughout life – both in terms of total amount of sleep needed (from 16.5 down to 5 hours) and the time at which it is taken.

AGE	NIGHT	DAY	TOTAL	NAPS
1 week	9.5	7.5	16.5	4
1 month	8.5	7	15.5	3
3 months	10	5	15	3
6 months	11	3.25	14.25	2
9 months	11	3	14	2
1 year	11.25	2.5	13.75	2
18 months	11.25	2.25	13.5	1
2 years	11	2	13	1
3 years	10.5	1.5	12	1
4 years	11.5		11.5	
5–9 years	10–11		10–11	
10–15 years	9–10		9–10	
15–18 years	8–9		8–9	
Young adults	7–8		7–8	
40–60 years	6–8		6–8	
60–80 years	4–5	1	5–6	1

Breathing is irregular and may be a little faster than it is in quiet sleep. In this state your baby is likely to make funny faces, grimaces, smiles and frowns, and they may make chewing or sucking movements.

THE BODY'S DEVELOPMENT DURING SLEEP

The capacity for growth and the strengthening of connections between nerve cells is the basis of brain development. The process of growth, known as plasticity, is believed to underlie the brain's capacity to control learning and memory.
In early life, sleep is crucial in the brain's development: research shows that sleep dramatically enhances changes in brain connections in young animals.

Plasticity occurs when events or information from the environment stimulate neurons. Animals allowed to sleep for six hours after a period of environmental stimulation develop twice the amount of brain change as animals kept awake during that post-stimulation period. In other words, sleep helps to consolidate the effects of waking experience on brain plasticity, converting memory into more permanent and enhanced forms. Further, the amount of plasticity in the brain depends on the amount of deep, quiet sleep, marked by large, slow brain waves. This is so-called non-REM sleep in which there is no rapid eye movement. This points to the importance of sleep for the development of the brain in young humans too.

THE CHANGING NATURE OF SLEEP

Sleep goes through several stages in the night. Stage 1 is a light sleep. During this, your muscles relax and your brain waves become rapid and irregular. In Stage 2, your brain waves become larger with bursts of electrical activity. Stages 3 and 4 are deep sleep during which your brain produces large slow waves: during this sleep, sometimes known as 'delta' or slow-wave sleep, you become more difficult to awaken. After an hour or so, you move into a highly active stage in which there are rapid eye movements – so-called REM sleep, in which brain waves are almost the same as when you are awake and you dream: this happens several times during a night's sleep.

SLEEPWALKING

Sleepwalking, otherwise known as somnambulism, is a sleep disorder in which there is walking or other activity while the person is seemingly still asleep. Sleepwalking can occur at any age but it is most common between the ages of six and 12 years, and it often runs in families: it is thought to be a genetic trait.

Sleepwalking usually occurs during deep non-REM sleep (stage 3 or stage 4 sleep) early in the night, but it can occur during REM sleep near morning. In a child the cause is usually unknown although often it seems to happen if there is sleep deprivation, anxiety or fatigue. By contrast, sleepwalking in adults is usually associated with a mental disorder or a reaction to prescribed or illegal drugs or alcohol.

Some medical conditions, such as some forms of epilepsy, are associated with sleepwalking.

Nocturnal activities

Episodes of sleepwalking may last anything from a few seconds to several minutes or even an hour. During an episode of sleepwalking a child's eyes are open, even though the child is actually asleep. They may be found sitting up wearing a blank facial expression, appearing to be awake. Or a child may actually get up and walk around. (Adults have been known to drive a car while actually asleep.) Sometimes a child may go to the lavatory, or they may pass urine in a wardrobe (presumably in the belief that they are in the lavatory), or they may get dressed or move furniture around. The child will have no recollection of the event upon awaking and they are likely to be confused and disorientated.

Investigating the cause

A very occasional episode of sleepwalking in a child does not need investigation. But if your child has frequent episodes your GP could refer your child to a specialist for further examination to rule out other disorders such as epilepsy. A psychological opinion may help to assess any causes such as undue stress or anxiety.

Treatment is not necessary unless an underlying condition is present. But safety measures may be necessary to prevent injury. You may need to move furniture or electrical cords to reduce the risk of tripping or falling. It may be necessary to put a safety gate at the top of a staircase. Short-acting tranquillisers may help to reduce the frequency of sleepwalking.

Sleepwalking: in the genes?
Scientists currently believe that people with a certain form of a gene responsible for the immune system are more susceptible to sleepwalking.

IT'S NOT TRUE!

'It is dangerous to wake a sleepwalker'

It used to be commonly said that it is dangerous to waken someone sleepwalking. In fact, it is not. However, it is common for a child to be confused or disoriented for a while after being awoken. It is also quite possible for a child to be injured while sleepwalking, usually because of tripping, falling over or bumping into furniture.

Helping your child to get a good night's sleep

If your child often suffers disturbed sleep – in which case you probably have disturbed sleep too – you may find that good 'sleep hygiene' holds the solution:

- Encourage your child to use bed for sleeping only – not for reading or watching television.

- Never use 'going to bed' as a punishment.

- Ensure the bedroom is not too warm and avoid extremes of temperature.

- Encourage a regular bedtime and getting up time, even at weekends. This helps to establish a consistent sleep rhythm.

- Ensure your child gets an amount of sleep appropriate for his or her age (see chart on page 86).

- Encourage your child to take regular daily exercise, preferably in the evenings but not for 30 minutes prior to bedtime.

- Discourage heavy meals within two hours of bedtime. A light snack such as milk, cheese or crackers at bedtime may be helpful. Do not give excessive fluids prior to bedtime.

- Discourage stimulants (such as cola, tea, cocoa, chocolates) within a few hours of bedtime.

- Accept occasional nights of sleeplessness as being normal.

Preventing sleepwalking

In some cases, sleepwalking in childhood simply stops. In other cases, it does not but there are ways to prevent sleepwalking taking hold in the first place. It is important that children do not become sleep deprived: ensure regular bedtimes and good sleep hygiene (see box). Try also to prevent children becoming fatigued or subject to too much stress or anxiety.

UNDERSTANDING TEENAGE SLEEP RHYTHMS

Teenagers tend to be 'night owls' and most like to go to bed late. Yet they still need their 8–10 hours' sleep. This is because teenagers usually have longer circadian rhythms than adults have – typically 25 or 26 hours a day. But, on average, teenagers sleep for only six hours: a 2–4 hour deficit every night. The tendency to stay up later and later until the sleep/wake cycle is almost reversed is sometimes called the Delayed Sleep Phase Syndrome (DSPS). Because teenagers need more sleep than adults do they usually compensate for sleep loss during the week by sleeping late whenever they can – especially at weekends. This can create a vicious cycle, which increases their difficulty getting up in the morning. Because most teenagers, like adults, need to operate on a daytime schedule, day/night reversal causes serious problems for college students who miss classes or workers who fall asleep on the job.

Hormone release during adolescent sleep

Sleep is especially important for teenagers as the release of certain hormones, especially growth hormone, increases during puberty. Growth hormones, along with testosterone, follicle-stimulating hormone and luteinising hormone are released mainly during sleep. These hormones are important in teenagers for physical and mental growth and development. So it is essential that they sleep properly.

AN ADULT'S SLEEP NEEDS

How much sleep does the average adult need? Most adults need seven to eight hours sleep, although some people need only five hours whilst others need ten hours of sleep each night. Sleep needs also vary depending upon circumstances. For example, women in the first three months of pregnancy often need more sleep. The amount of sleep needed also increases if someone has been short of sleep in previous days. Getting too little sleep creates a 'sleep debt' – like being overdrawn at the bank. Eventually, you have to repay that debt to your body by catching up on sleep. Failure to do so leads to reduced reaction time, inability to concentrate and impaired judgement.

MALE AND FEMALE SLEEP PATTERNS

As they age, men typically get less deep sleep. By age 45 they have nearly lost the ability to fall into deep sleep. After 50 a man's total sleep declines by about 27 minutes with each decade of age. Pre-menopausal women get more deep sleep than men do, but after the menopause there is little difference. Deep sleep in men under 25 is about 20 per cent of a night's sleep. From age 25 to 35 this falls to about 12 per cent. After age 35 it is less than five per cent.

During deep sleep your blood pressure and heart rate are lower. So deep sleep allows a temporary relief for your cardiovascular system. Ways to boost deep sleep include having a hot bath before bed, which increases body heat, and exercising at least 20 minutes three or four times a week.

THE POWER OF NAPPING

Most of us have experienced the mid-afternoon slump, even when we've slept well. This suggests that our bodies may be meant to nap. Afternoon naps, or siestas, are a way of life in many warm countries. North European culture is unlikely to adopt this lifestyle, but an occasional restorative nap may be very helpful. It seems that it may help you to tap into a reserve of alertness when there isn't an opportunity for a longer sleep.

A nap of 15 minutes or so can improve alertness, sharpen memory and reduce fatigue. If you have had too little sleep the previous night or if you know that you are going to lose sleep tonight, a nap can be restorative, hence the term 'power nap'. It can even make the difference between life and death if you are planning to drive a long distance with a sleep deficit. But a nap is not a substitute for a full night's sleep: it is merely a short-term solution. If you find it difficult to sleep at night you are probably best avoiding naps.

SLEEP DISRUPTION

Constantly disrupted or frequent lack of sleep can lead to depression, health problems, poor work performance, road traffic accidents, and marriage and family problems. Common causes are shift work, babies needing attention through the night and worries about work, money, family or relationships. People who frequently travel around the world on business can be affected by jet-lag-related health problems.

Night shifts: harmful to health?

Night shift workers have less effective sleep because it is not synchronised with the body's circadian rhythm. The worker has to work when the body expects to sleep, and sleep when the body expects to be active. As a result, sleep is often short or interrupted. As each working day goes by sleep deprivation accumulates and sleepiness at work becomes worse, resulting in fatigue. The situation is even worse if there are constant changes in the shift-working pattern, such as a week of night-time work followed by a week of daytime work. Stress becomes greater and greater and has an adverse effect on health.

Violent behaviour during sleep

Violent behaviour during sleep (VBS) is uncommon and affects about two per cent of adults. The features of this disorder are violent and/ or injurious behaviour during sleep. Both lifestyle and heredity play a role in causing this disorder. People with a mood or anxiety disorder as well as other abnormal sleep behaviour are more likely to have VBS. The condition may be psychological but if there is an underlying physical cause doctors are likely to treat the condition as a medical one.

SLEEP IN OLD AGE

Average sleep needs in later years can drop dramatically. Elderly people seem to get by quite satisfactorily on about five hours sleep at night, although this is usually supplemented by naps during the day. The elderly complain more often than the young do of both difficulty sleeping and daytime drowsiness. They also have a disproportionately high number of prescriptions for sleeping drugs. There are changes in the amount of deep sleep and REM sleep that the elderly experience each night, and their sleep patterns differ from sleep in the young in several ways:

- The elderly experience many brief arousals during the night.
- With age comes a loss of the deepest levels of non-REM sleep (stage 3 and 4 deep sleep).
- The elderly tend to have more daytime naps.
- With age there is less of a drop in body temperature during sleep.
- The elderly prefer earlier bedtimes and earlier waking-up times.

CHANGING CIRCADIAN RHYTHMS

Scientists do not yet have a full answer as to if, or how, hormone levels alter circadian rhythms in the elderly. The timing of the circadian rhythm of the secretion of two hormones, plasma melatonin and cortisol, occurs at a significantly earlier clock hour in older people than in young adults. However, this does not necessarily point to a causal role for these hormone changes in the sleep disruption associated with ageing.

Changes in the body temperature cycle in older people also influence their sleep/wake cycle. The rhythms

of core body-temperature changes occur at an earlier hour in older people, which probably accounts for why elderly people often feel more alert in the morning but sleepier later.

FACTORS HAMPERING SLEEP IN THE ELDERLY

The elderly tend to have a decreased ability to sleep, which can be for a number of reasons.

- **Sleep apnoea** This is the term for the stopping of breathing during sleep. Disruption of the breathing causes brief arousals to allow breathing to begin again, usually without full consciousness. It is more common in the elderly, especially if overweight, and affects more men than women.
- **Myoclonic activity** This term refers to muscle jerking, which briefly awakens the sleeper. It is more common in the elderly.
- **Medical problems** The elderly have more medical problems such as breathing problems, heart failure,

Restorative afternoon napping
Older people who have a short nap in the afternoon enjoy increased wakefulness in the evening and improved sleep quality at night.

gastric reflux and chronic pain (from arthritis, for example), which prevent them sleeping well.

- **Psychiatric illnesses** Such illnesses commonly impair sleep. One good example is dementia in which there is often an increase in agitation and disorientation at night. This is a common cause for nursing home placement as families find they are unable to deal with the active behaviour through the night.
- **Poor sleep habits** As with people of any age, poor sleep habits, such as an irregular sleep schedule, evening consumption of nicotine, caffeine or alcohol, or an uncomfortable sleeping environment, can lead to poor sleep. Overuse of sleeping pills can cause impaired sleep. Also, in the elderly there may be a tendency to spend too much time in bed, impairing sleep at night.

In addition, as many as 65 per cent of elderly people wake up several times a night to go to the lavatory.

GETTING HELP TO IMPROVE SLEEP

If an elderly person has difficulty sleeping night after night, there are several checks that a doctor can do. These include:

- having the person's spouse or partner or care staff observe breathing during sleep for signs of sleep apnoea (snoring or brief periods of not breathing);
- checking for abnormalities of heart rhythm;
- checking for abnormalities of body temperature.

Sleep apnoea frequently goes undiagnosed. Research suggests that at least one in five elderly men have the condition, and the figure may even be as high as two in three. Estimates for elderly women range from one in five to one in two. If there is evidence of sleep apnoea (heavy snoring with daytime sleepiness), or restless legs during sleep, or if standard treatment is not effective, the doctor may suggest a more in-depth evaluation in a sleep laboratory, where the patient's sleep is monitored through the night.

EXPLODING THE ALCOHOL MYTH

If you rely on alcohol to help you sleep you are likely to find that small amounts of alcohol become less effective at helping you fall asleep and that you need to drink more as time goes on. This is because your brain cells become used to the paralysing effect of alcohol. Drinking a large amount of alcohol can cause you to pass out, which is not real

sleep but a state of poisoning from which it can be difficult to be awoken. When the brain of a person in this state is monitored with an EEG, normal stages of sleep are absent.

Drinking heavily at bedtime prevents REM-sleep and therefore dreaming. With prolonged heavy alcohol use, REM-sleep begins to occur fitfully in the early hours of the morning. At this time your sleep is restless and you find that you wake up easily. With time, falling asleep also becomes more difficult. You find that you wake up in the small hours then find it difficult to go back to sleep. Alcohol is also associated with sleep apnoea.

RESTLESS LEG SYNDROME

Restless leg syndrome (RLS) is a common condition in which there is aching or fidgety, prickling sensations in the leg muscles,

especially the calves, whilst in bed. The only relief is to get up and walk which, in severe cases, leads to considerable sleep disruption. It affects mainly the middle-aged and elderly, pregnant women and people who smoke heavily or consume a lot of caffeine. The cause is usually unknown, but the remedy of iron and vitamin deficiencies, which are quite common in elderly sufferers, sometimes helps. There are also prescribed medications, such as levodopa, which may prove effective.

WAKE-UP TIME

People who wake early tend to be bright and busy first thing in the morning, while others have to drag themselves awake. There is no optimum time to get up in the morning, but if you are feeling stressed an extra 20 or 30 minutes sleeping could make a difference.

60-80 YEARS

Understanding and treating sleep problems

The treatment of sleep problems in the elderly naturally depends on the cause, but could include:

- Ensuring that the sleep environment is comfortable and that the bedroom is not too hot or too cold.
- Avoiding nicotine, caffeine, alcohol and liquids in the evening and at bedtime.
- Treating medical problems such as lung disease and heart failure.
- Treating psychiatric problems such as depression.
- Avoiding the overuse of sleeping pills.

- Restricting the use of the bedroom to sleep only – not for reading or watching television.
- Using relaxing bedtime rituals to signal that it is almost time to go to sleep; dimming the lights, soaking in a warm bath or drinking warm milk before bed.
- Encouraging good sleep hygiene, such as a regular bedtime and getting up time, together with an afternoon nap.

Because sleep patterns change with advancing years, adjusting the expectations of what a night's sleep will be like can also help.

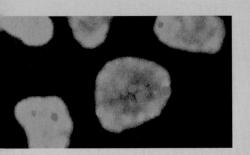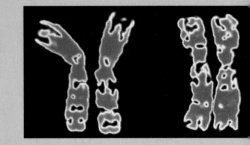

3

What happens
when things go wrong

Knowing what can go wrong

As medicine overcomes the problems of infectious diseases and as society takes on the challenges of poverty and malnutrition, an increasing proportion of the disorders of infancy and childhood have become genetic in origin.

Genetic diseases and disorders may be caused by problems with genes or chromosomes. Some disorders are inherited and some are not. Many are apparent at birth, others only become obvious as a child grows, or develop in later life. Some genetic disorders are inevitable and unavoidable; others are not.

Many disorders of genetic origin are rare, but the total number of people with a genetic disorder is significant. About 2 per cent of the population have a genetic disorder at birth and 5 per cent are predestined to develop a genetic disease by the age of 25. Some 60 per cent of all adults develop some kind of condition at some point in their lifetime that arises from a genetic predisposition to a disorder.

MORE COMMON

DOWN'S SYNDROME 143 PER 100,000 BABIES (1 IN 700)	SPINA BIFIDA 100 PER 100,000 (1 IN 1000)
POLYCYSTIC KIDNEY DISEASE 100 PER 100,000 (1 IN 1000) *PKD is usually diagnosed in* *early adulthood.*	CYSTIC FIBROSIS 40 PER 100,000 BABIES (1 IN 2500)

Onset of the disorder is generally triggered by some factor to do with lifestyle or the environment. Examples are asthma and high blood pressure.

GENETIC DISORDERS BEFORE BIRTH

When we think of the complexity of development from a single joined egg and sperm to a newborn baby, it is amazing that so many babies are born

Genetic diseases and disorders

The figures given are an indication of the number of people born with these genetic disorders in the UK each year. Many genetic disorders are identified at birth, but some, as with the kidney disorders listed, may only become apparent later in life.

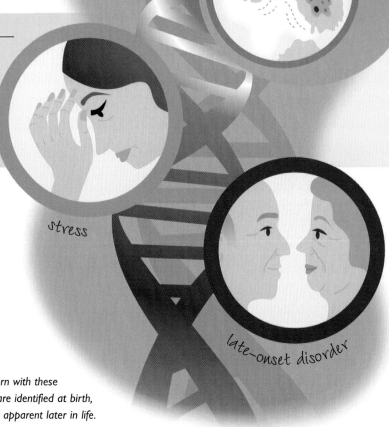

genetic disorders at birth

environment

cancer

stress

late-onset disorder

without problems. When a miscarriage occurs, it is generally because something has gone wrong with the development of the embryo. Six out of every ten embryos miscarried during the first 12 weeks of pregnancy have a genetic abnormality of some kind.

DISORDERS IN BABIES

Conditions recognised as soon as a baby is born or soon after have a variety of causes. Problems such as spina bifida, congenital heart defects and cleft lip usually occur because of a mixture of genetic and environmental factors. Less often, a baby is born with a combination of birth defects, such as a heart defect and eye abnormality. These problems are more likely to have a single cause, such as a specific chromosome or single gene defect, or a cause like a blood clot or toxic medication.

Developmental problems

Also present at birth, or appearing in the first few months of life, are more subtle abnormalities such as hearing or vision abnormalities, difficulties in feeding, or slow growth. A thorough investigation can help to identify the

In Europe and North America, one third or more of paediatric hospital admissions today are as a result of birth defects and genetic disease.

Another set of problems can become apparent at puberty. A wide variety of genes come into play to transform a child into an adult and it may be at this point that a problem with a genetic origin becomes apparent for the first time.

Some conditions are defined as disorders by their timing. Examples of this are early or delayed puberty. When onset of puberty is not within the usual age ranges (between 10 and 14 years in girls and 12 to 15 years in boys), appropriate investigations are made and hormone treatments prescribed if necessary.

DISORDERS THAT DEVELOP LATER IN LIFE

Disorders that develop after early childhood – often in adulthood – are usually multifactorial. The term 'multifactorial' (meaning 'several causes') indicates that

LESS COMMON

DUCHENNE MUSCULAR DYSTROPHY	HAEMOPHILIA	HUNTINGTON'S DISEASE	SCID (SEVERE COMBINED IMMUNODEFICIENCY)
29 PER 100,000 MALE BABIES (1 IN 3500) Males with this disorder have the symptoms but females may be carriers.	20 PER 100,000 MALE BABIES (1 IN 5000) The symptoms affect males only, though females may be carriers.	6.5 PER 100,000 (1 IN 15,000) This is a late-onset disorder, with symptoms generally appearing in middle age.	1.5 PER 100,000 (1 IN 66,500 BABIES)
	ALPORT'S SYNDROME 20 PER 100,000 (1 IN 5000)	ALBINISM 6 PER 100,000 BABIES (1 IN 17,000)	

cause of these problems. Growth and development are monitored in order to identify babies who are developing more slowly than they should (see page 107).

PROBLEMS IN CHILDHOOD AND PUBERTY

Childhood and youth are times of rapid growth and continuing development. Problems that were not always apparent when a child was younger, such as nerve or muscle damage, may now become noticeable for the first time. A developmental delay may affect a child's speech and language, motor skills, or personal and social skills. A child with 'global' delay has delay in all these areas of development.

a disorder has a combination of genetic and other causes. There is potential for a multifactorial disorder when a combination of small variations in genes makes up what is in effect a genetic predisposition to a certain disorder. This genetic predisposition may or may not be activated (resulting in development of the disorder) by some other non-genetic cause (often never identified). Multifactorial disorders range from the minor to the very serious.

Disorders triggered by environment and lifestyle

Multifactorial disorders may be linked to pollutants in the environment. Notable examples are allergies and asthma, which occur in reaction to environmental stimulants.

The longer we live, the more environmental pollutants we are exposed to; as a result, multifactorial conditions mostly develop in adulthood, though some occur earlier.

Multifactorial disorders are often triggered by lifestyle choices. For instance, too much stress can contribute to the development of a mental disorder such as depression, to which some people have a genetic predisposition. Over-indulgence in alcohol or nicotine can also trigger a multifactorial disorder. Excessive alcohol consumption may lead to liver damage or diabetes; smoking causes lung cancer, emphysema and heart disease. By keeping to a healthy diet and exercising sensibly, avoiding too much alcohol and not smoking, the chances of developing a multifactorial disorder can be reduced significantly.

CANCER

All cancers are genetic in that they involve changes to the genes, but only a small percentage of them are inherited. In many common cancers – such as colon cancer and breast cancer – tumours develop when mutations occur in both copies of a gene (one copy is inherited from each parent) that regulates normal cell growth and replication.

Sporadic cancers that are not inherited

Most cancers are sporadic, that is they happen because we accumulate mutations randomly as we age. Sporadic cancers usually occur later in life (late middle age onwards) because we are born with two normal copies of the gene and it takes many years to accumulate sufficient mutations in both copies to cause cancer.

Inherited cancers

In some families, however, there is an inherited predisposition to cancer. About 5 per cent of cancers fall into a pattern of familial transmission, suggesting the cancer is inherited. Indications that this may be the case include several closely related family members with the same cancer or genetically associated cancers (for example, breast and ovary, bowel and lining of the uterus), or two family members with the same rare cancer.

Affected individuals within these families inherit one copy of the mutant gene from an affected parent. Tumours tend to develop at a much earlier age than in sporadic cancers because individuals are born with a mutation in one copy of the gene already. Once they accumulate a mutation in the second (normal) copy of the gene, a tumour can develop.

Different types of genetic disorders

AUTOSOMAL DOMINANT INHERITED DISORDER This type occurs when an abnormal dominant gene inherited from one parent passes on the disorder it carries to the child. (An autosome is any chromosome that is not a sex chromosome.)
AUTOSOMAL RECESSIVE INHERITED DISORDER Someone with a genetic disorder inherited in this way has inherited two recessive genes, one from each parent, which only when together combine to produce symptoms of the disorder.
X-LINKED INHERITED DISORDER 'X-linked' inheritance of a disorder usually occurs when a matching abnormal recessive gene is on the X chromosome of both parents, and both genes are inherited by a child.
CHROMOSOMAL DISORDER Chromosomal disorders are not generally inherited. There may be a missing or extra chromosome, or the problem may be caused by an abnormal structure within a chromosome.
MULTIFACTORIAL DISORDER This type of disorder is caused by a combination of an inherited genetic predisposition and other factors – often involving the environment or the lifestyle of the patient. The disorder develops when 'other factors' trigger the genetic predisposition.

Some inherited cancer syndromes are marked by predisposition to tumours in specific tissues that are individually very rare in sporadic cancers. For example, von Hippel-Landau disease predisposes to cancers of the kidney, brain, spinal cord and retina. For some of the syndromes the genes and the mechanisms involved have been identified. Affected patients can be offered testing to identify the inherited mutation and unaffected relatives may be offered tests to determine whether they have also inherited the familial mutation before tumours develop. Such presymptomatic or predictive testing can lead to earlier cancer detection and more successful treatment.

Rarely, cancers result from the inheritance of two recessive genes. An example is the rare skin disease xeroderma pigmentosum, in which the patient's skin is unable to repair normal damage from sunlight, making the patient very susceptible to skin cancer.

Meet the genetic health and developmental experts

As well as the experts who deal with patients face to face – doctors, counsellors and nurses – there are, behind the scenes, the various laboratory specialists who help their fellow professionals to arrive at a complete diagnosis.

GENETIC NURSE

This is a specialist nurse who has additional training in genetics. The genetic nurse works very like a genetic counsellor in conjunction with a medical geneticist or other specialist in a variety of settings. Some genetic nurses also work independently. Genetic nurses are more common in some countries than genetic counsellors or associates.

GENETIC COUNSELLOR OR GENETIC ASSOCIATE

A genetic counsellor is not a medical doctor, but usually has a degree in science or psychology and postgraduate training in genetic counselling. Genetic counsellors often assist medical geneticists. They are trained to be non-directive towards their clients when discussing the client's possible future options. They are not trained to make a diagnosis. Genetic counsellors sometimes work in prenatal settings explaining genetic screening, or with a geneticist in a specialist hospital.

In recent years, genetic counsellors have been expanding their roles into other settings. In the specialist area of cancer genetics, for example, a genetic counsellor may work with an oncologist on an oncology unit. Some genetic counsellors have moved into research, where they become specialists in a specific condition or group of conditions. A genetic counsellor will refer a family seeking information and advice to a medical geneticist or other specialist if a diagnosis is unclear, or if the counsellor perceives that a client needs more support than the counsellor is able to give.

LABORATORY SPECIALISTS

• **Cytogeneticists** are specialists in chromosomes and chromosomal testing. They usually work in a laboratory. Some work in research, trying to understand how chromosome abnormalities come about and defining particular abnormalities.

MEDICAL GENETICIST

This is a doctor who diagnoses rare genetic diseases and is a resource for information about these diseases for other doctors, specialists and patients. Medical geneticists are often paediatricians; increasingly, doctors specialising in obstetrics and gynaecology, oncology, neurology, gastroenterology and other medical specialities are becoming genetic specialists too. Most geneticists are based in a specialist and/or teaching hospital.

• **Biochemical geneticists** are specialists in metabolic abnormalities. They may work in clinical settings or in laboratories. They have a special understanding of the biochemistry of the body.
• **Molecular geneticists** generally work in laboratories, looking directly at the DNA that makes up the genes. Many work in research and are specialists in only one or a few disorders. They may develop tremendous knowledge of the mutations that have been discovered for a particular disease and the kinds of problems that occur. Others work in hospital laboratories.

DEVELOPMENTAL PAEDIATRICIAN

This is a medically trained doctor who has then undertaken further training in the care of children and developmental disorders in particular.

DEVELOPMENTAL PSYCHOLOGIST

This is someone with a degree in psychology who has gone on to take a specialist interest in the development of the child's mind, including developmental disorders.

FINDING OUT WHAT IS WRONG

In this section we will give an overview of the types of tests currently available for genetic disorders and for developmental disorders, many of which are genetic in origin. Accuracy of testing varies depending on the nature of the test, the disorder being investigated, and the level of knowledge and understanding that scientists currently have of the disorder. However, recent and continuing advances in medical research mean that the variety and accuracy of genetic testing is improving all the time.

Medical history and examination

When trying to find out what is wrong, the doctor aims to identify symptoms that suggest particular disorders and then to substantiate a possible diagnosis by examining the patient and arranging tests.

CONSULTATION WITH THE GP

The GP is usually the first port of call for any medical problem. The doctor may be approached by the patient or by a parent accompanying a child. Developmental problems or hearing and vision problems may be noticed by parents or by teachers at school, or picked up in a routine screening by the GP or health visitor.

Taking a full medical history

The first part of the diagnostic process involves taking a thorough history. Not only will this involve discussing the symptoms themselves, but also other relevant areas of the patient's life.

ASKING ABOUT SYMPTOMS

The doctor will ask for a full description of the patient's symptoms. For example, in the case of pain, when the pain first started; whether it is constant or intermittent; if intermittent, when it comes on; whether any particular activity brings it on; how severe the pain is (for example, does it keep the patient awake); how the pain could best be described (for example, as a dull ache or stabbing); where the pain is localised; whether the pain spreads to another part of the body.

Playing detective

Some conditions cause a variety of symptoms which, if several of them occur together, may suggest a certain disorder. For example, if the thyroid gland that produces hormones involved in regulating metabolism is overactive, the symptoms noticed may include weight loss despite increased appetite, shaking of the hands, poor tolerance of heat, sweating and feeling anxious. If the thyroid is underactive, symptoms may include tiredness, an increase in weight, and poor tolerance of the cold.

Symptoms can be vague and even atypical, that is, differing from what might be expected for the disorder

What are the special problems associated with diagnosing symptoms in small children?

Diagnosing an illness in a small child can be a challenge because the child is unable to describe the symptoms. Therefore, the way a disease presents itself can be different in a small child from the presentation in older children and adults. This can be seen, for example, in the condition cystitis. Symptoms usually include increased frequency of urination and burning discomfort on passing urine. It is the patient's description of these symptoms that guides the doctor's diagnosis. However, a small child may simply go off food and be generally off-colour, and these vague symptoms can be explained by a variety of illnesses.
A doctor should be aware of this and therefore carry out a urine test when such vague symptoms arise.

ASK THE EXPERT

that turns out to be the cause. When this happens it is often not at all easy to reach a diagnosis. Even so, in most cases the doctor is able to piece together enough information from the history, examination and tests to make an initial diagnosis.

FURTHER INFORMATION NEEDED

In addition to covering the symptoms, the doctor may ask about some or all of the following. Not only may this help the doctor in making a diagnosis, but it will also give information on possible causes or factors that are contributing to or worsening the disorder.

Individual and family medical background

The doctor will want to know about symptoms and conditions experienced by the patient in the past. The doctor will also ask about the health of family members, in particular parents, brothers and sisters, and grandparents. This will include whether any of them died at an early age and whether there is a family history of certain health problems, such as heart disease

Looking for spinal defects
A paediatrician examines a young girl's vertebral column, looking for abnormalities, as part of a physical examination.

or cancer. A history of any specific genetic conditions will also be noted. When necessary, the doctor will arrange for a geneticist to take a family history (see page 100).

A social history

This is an important part of taking a medical history.

- The doctor will ask whether the patient smokes, as this can play a role in the development and progression of many disorders, in particular coronary artery disease, peripheral vascular disease (in which the blood vessels that supply the limbs become narrowed) and certain cancers. It can worsen existing diseases, such as asthma. Many of these disorders have a genetic component.
- The doctor will also ask about an individual's average weekly alcohol intake. Alcohol can cause or play a role in the development of various disorders, such as liver disease and diabetes.
- The doctor may also ask for information on a patient's usual levels of exercise as well as the patient's diet.
- In adults, information about occupation and working environment may be required, because some jobs can play a role in the development of certain disorders. For example, asthma may develop as a result of exposure to certain materials in the workplace, including particular types of glue.

Special issues concerning children

For younger children, the doctor may review the child's development history, in varying detail depending on the disorder. The doctor may also make note of what immunisations the child has had. These points may not always be relevant to the current problem but give the doctor a more comprehensive picture of the child's health.

THE PHYSICAL EXAMINATION

The doctor will use the physical examination to look for further clues that will support the information gleaned from the history findings and help to make a diagnosis.

Looking for physical signs

The doctor may carry out a general examination, or may focus on part of the body, such as the lungs or the cardiovascular system. Pulse, blood pressure and checking for swelling of the lymph nodes are all commonly included in the examination. Some disorders cause an array of signs affecting various parts of the body. For example, severe hypertension may damage the blood vessels at the back of the eye, so a finding of high blood pressure may be followed by an eye examination.

Searching for the cause of a suspected disorder

In addition to looking for the features of the disease, the doctor may use the examination to help look for a cause of the disorder. For example, a doctor who suspects anaemia will check the patient's nails (which may be spoon-shaped when anaemia is caused by iron deficiency) or look for jaundice (yellow coloration of the skin and whites of the eyes) which can occur in haemolytic anaemia (a disorder caused by the excessive breakdown of red blood cells).

GENERAL TESTS

Sometimes, there is no specific pattern of signs and symptoms, or the symptoms are very vague. In these cases general tests, often blood tests, are used to look for clues to a possible diagnosis.

SCREENING FOR DISORDERS

Developmental disorders and other conditions may be picked up by routine screening. Screening aims to pick up conditions early in the disease process, before they are causing symptoms, and so improve the likely outcome. Examples of conditions that may be picked up in this way include high blood pressure, diabetes mellitus (sometimes diagnosed following routine urine analysis that picks up sugar), certain breast diseases (picked up on mammograms) and precancerous changes of the cervix (detected on cervical smears).

REFERRAL TO A SPECIALIST

A GP may refer the patient to see a hospital-based doctor either for help in making a diagnosis or for treatment once the diagnosis is made. The specialist may have special expertise in a particular area, such as heart disease (a cardiologist), or may have a wider field of work, such as general paediatrics. In the case of rare disorders, the specialist is likely to have more experience of an unusual condition than a GP and so be more likely to recognise the pattern of symptoms.

Specialists will also have more ready access to certain tests, such as endoscopy, in which a viewing instrument is used to look internally at parts of the digestive tract, or coronary angiography, in which the passage of dye through the arteries supplying the heart muscle is observed to see whether the blood vessels are narrowed (as occurs in coronary artery disease).

EVALUATION BY A GENETICIST

Geneticists rely on a very thorough review of medical records and examination to make their diagnoses. A patient's appointment with a geneticist may well last an hour or more.

Obtaining a family history

The patient will probably be asked to bring family history information and pictures of any other affected family members to the appointment. Sometimes the patient will be contacted ahead of the appointment with the geneticist and a family history will be taken in advance in the patient's home or over the phone. If other affected family members are identified, the patient may be asked to obtain permission from them for the geneticist to read their medical records. This can usually be done by the affected family member writing to their doctor, or signing a release of information form, which specifies which records they agree to have their own doctor release to the geneticist. If this is not done prior to the appointment, it may be requested then, and there will need to be a further consultation with the geneticist after the records have been obtained, in order to review the findings.

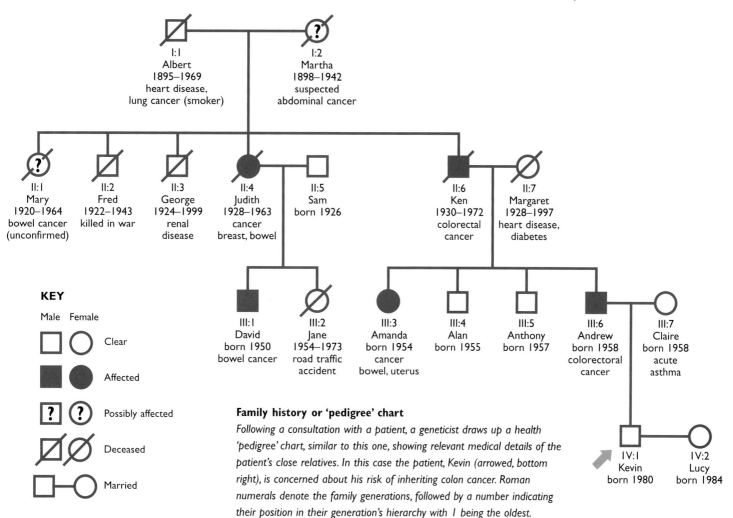

KEY

Male Female

☐ ○ Clear

■ ● Affected

☐? ○? Possibly affected

▨ ⊘ Deceased

☐—○ Married

Family history or 'pedigree' chart

Following a consultation with a patient, a geneticist draws up a health 'pedigree' chart, similar to this one, showing relevant medical details of the patient's close relatives. In this case the patient, Kevin (arrowed, bottom right), is concerned about his risk of inheriting colon cancer. Roman numerals denote the family generations, followed by a number indicating their position in their generation's hierarchy with 1 being the oldest.

For further information on taking a family history, see page 46 onwards.

The physical examination

The physical examination conducted by the geneticist may involve the following:

- taking measurements of parts of the body such as the face, arms and legs, and noting the various body proportions;
- listening to the heart;
- some neurological testing, depending on the condition that is being evaluated;
- taking photographs to include with the family's medical genetics records.

Geneticists look for variations from the norm, some of which are small, subtle differences that would not be detected by anyone who is untrained. Some of these variations will be usual for the family, others will be specific to the affected person and the condition being assessed. In order to understand what is common to the family and what is part of the syndrome, it is often helpful for the geneticist to examine other family members, such as parents or brothers and sisters.

Additional testing

After the geneticist has reviewed all the information and performed the physical examination, the geneticist will then summarise the impressions gained. There may be several possible explanations for the problems observed, and additional testing may be recommended to clarify the situation. This may involve the patient visiting another specialist; for example, if a heart murmur is detected, the geneticist may want a cardiologist to verify the specific abnormality. If a child is not growing well, the geneticist may ask an endocrinologist to check the levels of the child's growth hormone. In addition, genetic testing may be suggested, which usually requires a blood sample. The geneticist should explain the testing that is being carried out and why it is being done, and then talk with the patient again after the test results are available.

Tests before birth

Prenatal tests are screening and diagnostic procedures carried out on women who are pregnant, in order to discover whether the developing fetus has any genetic or other abnormalities that are serious enough to be a matter of concern.

WHY HAVE PRENATAL TESTS?

Prenatal testing takes place during the first few months of pregnancy, and is offered to all expecting couples in order to try to detect any problems early in the pregnancy. Many couples choose to undergo prenatal testing because there is an established family history of genetic disease, but most couples taking part have no family history of particular problems.

Some maternal infections pose serious risks to the fetus, such as rubella, syphilis, hepatitis B and HIV, and prenatal testing can be offered if any of these are suspected. It is also important for the mother-to-be to mention to her doctor anything she may have been exposed to in the first 12 weeks of her pregnancy, perhaps before she knew she was pregnant, that she may be concerned about. This might include environmental hazards, prescribed or recreational drugs, or immoderate amounts of alcohol.

Another risk factor is the mother's age: a woman's risk of a chromosome problem in a pregnancy, such as Down's syndrome, increases with age. There is a gradual increase in risk from 1 in 1500 risk for a mother-to-be who is 20, to a risk of about 1 in 190 (0.5 per cent) for a mother who will be 35 when the baby is born. By the age of 45, the risk of having a child with a chromosome problem is about 1 in 20. The same screening tests are available to older mothers as to younger mothers, but older mothers can skip straight to the diagnostic testing if they wish, because they are more at risk.

PRENATAL SCREENING TESTS

Screening tests in general are designed to miss as few affected individuals as possible, but in doing so they pick up more individuals who 'screen positive' than will eventually turn out to have the problem. In other words, many more pregnant women will 'screen positive' than actually have a baby with a disorder.

There are several screening tests available at different points in the pregnancy to assess for genetic or other risks to the baby. Being screening tests, they will not tell the mother for sure if there is a problem, they will merely

What is a screening test?

A screening test is a test that is carried out on a large number of apparently healthy individuals to separate those who show indications of a particular disease from those who do not. A fetus or baby who screens positive for a disorder is always tested again using a different, more accurate diagnostic test for confirmation. For some babies who initially 'screen positive' for an abnormality, the more accurate diagnostic testing process will show that they do not have the disease or disorder in question.

ASK THE EXPERT

indicate whether more accurate diagnostic testing is needed. The tests are all designed to present as little danger as possible to the pregnancy.

Diagnostic testing is more accurate, but may put the pregnancy at some risk, so diagnostic testing is not in general encouraged in cases of women regarded as being at low risk of a pregnancy complication unless a screening test indicates that it is needed.

Maternal serum screening test

This is a blood test that is usually offered to women who are 14–16 weeks into pregnancy. It is also known as triple, quadruple or multiple marker screening. The test measures a number of protein markers that are in the blood of the mother-to-be as a result of the pregnancy. Levels of these markers are analysed, taking into account the mother's age, weight and ethnic background. The test provides a revised risk assessment of certain chromosome problems being present in the baby, and a risk level for an open neural tube defect (such as spina bifida). If the risk assessment for chromosome problems is above a set cut-off value, then diagnostic testing is offered. The main chromosome problems tested for are Down's syndrome (see page 144) and Edwards syndrome (trisomy 18, a severe mental retardation syndrome usually associated with multiple physical abnormalities, learning difficulties and a significantly shortened life span). The test will also indicate other much rarer chromosomal abnormalities.

Nuchal thickness screening

This specialised ultrasound test is performed at 10–11 weeks into pregnancy. It looks specifically at the thickness of the skin at the back of the fetus's neck (the nuchal fold). The thicker the nuchal fold, the greater the risk of the fetus having a chromosomal defect or a neural tube defect. If the risk is above a certain level, further diagnostic testing is offered. The benefit of this test is that it is usually offered a little earlier in pregnancy than the maternal serum screening test and so earlier diagnostic testing may be available for the mother.

PRENATAL DIAGNOSTIC TESTS

The tests a mother is offered depends on how much her baby is thought to be at risk of developing a genetic disorder. Testing is available for specific genetic conditions if there is a family history of a disorder, and for age-related conditions. The most common testing is for chromosome abnormalities such as Down's syndrome.

Testing for chromosome abnormalities

Chromosome testing involves obtaining a sample of fetal cells and growing the cells in a special nutrient culture medium. There is a waiting period of 10–14 days whilst the cells grow in culture. Cultured cells are harvested, chemically treated and stained on a microscope slide so the chromosomes are visible when viewed down the microscope. This process is known as preparing a complete 'chromosome spread'.

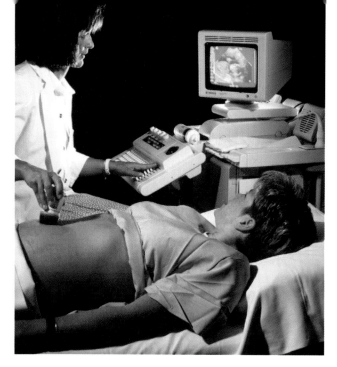

Ultrasound scan
Ultrasound scanning is a painless and safe way of imaging the uterus and the fetus inside. This scan is a routine check performed 16–18 weeks into the pregnancy. Visualisation of the fetus in this way can pick up many congenital abnormalities.

Cells are microscopically examined to assess the number of chromosomes and whether the chromosomes have any structural abnormalities, such as extra or missing pieces.

Fluorescent in situ hybridisation (FISH) testing

This is a relatively new method of chromosome analysis. It uses special fluorescent dyes or 'probes' which examine specific individual chromosomes.

• **Rapid prenatal FISH testing** FISH probes specific for chromosomes 21, 18 and for the sex chromosomes (X and Y) can be used to assess Down's syndrome (trisomy 21), Edwards syndrome (trisomy 18) or missing or extra sex chromosomes. The advantage is that this analysis does not require fetal cells to be grown in culture first and so the analysis can be completed much more quickly than standard chromosome testing (2–3 days for FISH compared with 10–14 days for standard chromosome analysis). The disadvantage is that rapid FISH gives

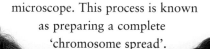

Taking a blood sample
If fetal abnormalities are detected by the ultrasound scan performed at 16–18 weeks, a blood sample is taken to follow up. Also at a later stage of pregnancy, blood tests may be performed to check for anaemia.

only a partial result, since only chromosomes 18, 21, X and Y (and sometimes 13 too) are assessed, and will not detect subtle structural abnormalities involving any other chromosomes. Rapid FISH is therefore often carried out in conjunction with standard chromosome analysis, as a two-part test where getting results quickly on the most common problems (chromosomes 18, 21, X and Y) is important.

• **FISH to detect 'microdeletions'** Some chromosome abnormalities involve the loss of tiny chromosome fragments that are too small to detect by conventional chromosome testing. These 'microdeletions' can be detected using specific FISH probes. This analysis requires cells to be grown in culture and all chromosomes that might be involved looked at, so it is no quicker than standard chromosome testing. However, because the FISH probes are so sensitive, abnormalities are detected that would be missed by standard testing. The tests are specific for particular syndromes which might be suspected after finding an ultrasound scan abnormality, or where there is a family history of a syndrome, such as a congenital heart defect.

PRENATAL SAMPLING TECHNIQUES

Samples of fetal tissue may be obtained in several ways, usually for the purpose of chromosome testing, but they may also be used for DNA analysis or biochemical analysis. For prenatal testing, the most commonly used and safest sampling procedures are chorionic villus sampling (CVS) and amniocentesis. Another method that is more risky for the fetus, but provides results more quickly in an emergency, is percutaneous umbilical blood sampling (PUBS).

Chorionic villus sampling (CVS)

Chorionic villi are microscopic finger-like projections that form part of the placenta. A sample is taken at 10–12 weeks of pregnancy and grown in a laboratory. The sample is collected via the vagina and cervix, or by means of a needle through the abdomen, depending on the position of the placenta and the preference of the expert performing the procedure. CVS samples may be tested by chromosome analysis (by conventional testing or rapid FISH), DNA or biochemical analysis. These tests are usually very accurate. Rarely, chromosome results

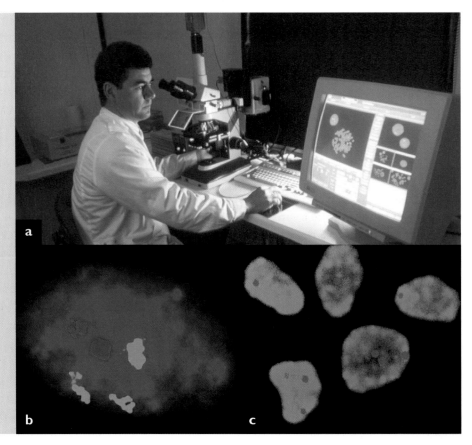

FISH testing

a The FISH technique enables individual chromosomes to be tagged with a fluorescent dye. This shows up in the cell nucleus when examined under a fluorescent light microscope. Here the geneticist has identified a chromosomal disorder caused by 'trisomy' – the existence of a third copy of a chromosome in addition to the normal two copies.

b This FISH micrograph (a photograph taken through a microscope) shows three copies of chromosome number 18 (coloured blue-green) within a cell nucleus (mid blue). This indicates the condition trisomy 18 (see page 101).

c The three pink number 21 chromosomes within each blue nucleus indicate Down's syndrome.

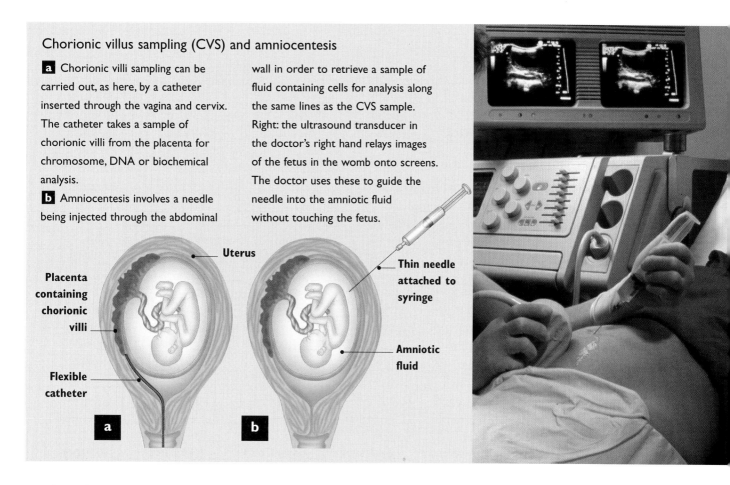

Chorionic villus sampling (CVS) and amniocentesis

a Chorionic villi sampling can be carried out, as here, by a catheter inserted through the vagina and cervix. The catheter takes a sample of chorionic villi from the placenta for chromosome, DNA or biochemical analysis.

b Amniocentesis involves a needle being injected through the abdominal wall in order to retrieve a sample of fluid containing cells for analysis along the same lines as the CVS sample. Right: the ultrasound transducer in the doctor's right hand relays images of the fetus in the womb onto screens. The doctor uses these to guide the needle into the amniotic fluid without touching the fetus.

Uterus

Placenta containing chorionic villi

Flexible catheter

Thin needle attached to syringe

Amniotic fluid

a

b

may be ambiguous because although the CVS being tested is from the placenta, which is grown by the fetus, some areas of placental tissue may have a slightly different chromosome make-up than the fetus itself. In such cases additional testing – usually by amniocentesis – is offered for clarification.

Amniocentesis

Amniocentesis is offered from 15 weeks of pregnancy. A sample of the amniotic fluid surrounding the baby is obtained by a needle passed through the mother's abdomen into the uterus. This fluid contains dead and dying skin cells from the fetus. These are isolated then tested by DNA, biochemical or rapid FISH analysis, or cultured for 10–14 days for conventional chromosome testing. Chromosome analysis is slightly more accurate than by CVS because the rare errors due to unusual chromosomal make-up of the placenta are avoided.

Percutaneous umbilical blood sampling (PUBS)

PUBS is offered at various times in a pregnancy when a sample of fetal blood is required. Chromosome testing can be carried out directly without culturing, so that results can be obtained faster. However, at 1 in 20 the risk of miscarriage is significantly higher, so this testing is usually only offered if there is at least as high a risk of a chromosomal abnormality in the pregnancy.

PREIMPLANTATION GENETIC DIAGNOSIS

PGD can only be offered to families with a genetic disease for which the diagnosis has been confirmed by genetic testing (usually DNA testing). An example might be parents of a child with cystic fibrosis, where the specific cystic fibrosis gene mutations have been confirmed in both carrier parents.

PGD requires in vitro fertilisation, that is, embryos are conceived outside the body. PGD involves production of several embryos; then a single cell is removed from each embryo at the 8 or 16-cell stage for rapid testing by DNA analysis. Removing one cell poses no risk to the embryo, but it enables identification of embryos that do not carry two copies of the cystic fibrosis mutation and therefore will not develop the disease. Unaffected embryos are then implanted in the mother's uterus.

Biochemical screening for newborns

Babies may be screened shortly after birth for a variety of congenital disorders, that may be inherited or arise from other causes. Biochemical screening tests involve the analysis of blood samples taken from babies, so are sometimes called 'blood spot' screening.

THE GUTHRIE SCREENING TEST FOR PHENYLKETONURIA (PKU)

The first newborn screening test was introduced in the USA in the 1960s by Dr Robert Guthrie. This was for phenylketonuria, an inherited defect of protein metabolism that causes an excess of the amino acid phenylalanine in the blood. Normally, phenylalanine is converted into another amino acid, tyrosine. In PKU this conversion does not take place and phenylalanine accumulates in the blood instead. This happens because the baby has mutations in both copies of the gene for phenylalanine hydroxylase, so the enzyme that converts phenylalanine to tyrosine does not work. An excess of phenylalanine damages the brain and nervous system. Treatment consists of a special diet low in phenylalanine.

SCREENING FOR HYPOTHYROIDISM

Screening for congenital hypothyroidism is also carried out by means of analysis of a blood sample. Congenital hypothyroidism is underactivity of the thyroid gland; it is occasionally inherited. Hypothyroidism in a baby can, like PKU, cause brain damage if untreated. Also like PKU, it can be successfully treated if diagnosed early.

DETECTING OTHER DISORDERS

All newborn babies in the UK are routinely screened for phenylketonuria and hypothyroidism. Biochemical screening tests for the following inherited or congenital conditions are also sometimes given to babies. None are yet routine for all babies in the UK, but they are given if there is a family history of the disorder or increased 'population risk' due to ethnic background.

- Disorders affecting haemoglobin, such as sickle cell disease (see page 152) and thalassaemia.
- Congenital adrenal hyperplasia, a condition that affects the reproductive organs of boys and girls.
- Galactosaemia, the inability to utilise the sugar galactose, which then builds up in the blood.
- Maple syrup urine disease (MSUD), a defect of amino acid metabolism that affects urine and leads to brain damage and death if untreated.
- Biotinidase deficiency, affecting vitamin B production.

THE WAY AHEAD

As the science of testing improves, a larger range of biochemical screening tests will become available. These will be able to detect many more conditions, although many doctors will not screen for disorders for which there is no effective treatment. Many US screening laboratories already possess a 'tandem mass spectrometer'. This is a machine that detects molecules by measuring their mass (weight). A tandem mass spectrometer can chart the biochemistry of a blood sample quickly and in great detail, increasing the number of disorders that can be detected, and improving the accuracy of the screening test. DNA chip technology may also add to the arsenal of potential screening methodologies. A DNA chip similar to a computer chip but fitted with DNA molecules may be able to probe a biological sample for genetic information on hundreds of potential disorders and indicate whether a baby has a genetic predisposition to one or more.

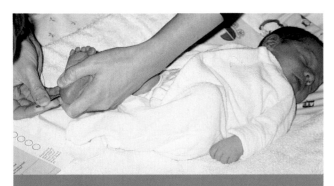

How the Guthrie test is performed

A few days after birth, samples of a baby's blood are gathered by transferring a few drops of blood from the baby's heel onto a piece of card called a Guthrie card. The card is then sent to a laboratory and tested to assess how much phenylalanine is in the blood. If the test indicates the possibility of the baby having PKU, further tests are carried out to establish whether or not the baby has the disorder.

Developmental monitoring

Infancy and childhood are times of great discovery when we develop both physical and social skills as well as acquiring knowledge at an incredible rate. A number of tests are routinely carried out to check a child's development and see that all is well.

WHAT ARE DEVELOPMENTAL DISORDERS?

Delays in childhood development may involve one or more of the following:

• hearing

• vision

• motor skills, both gross (large movements such as walking) and fine (precise movements and dexterity)

• language skills

• behaviour and emotional development.

Problems to do with physical growth are not classified by doctors as developmental disorders, but in practice height and weight are monitored along with the areas of development listed above. Many developmental disorders result from genetic abnormalities which may or may not be inherited. Some disorders become obvious at an early stage, while others take years to present symptoms.

MONITORING DEVELOPMENT

A child's development is monitored by formal assessments at specific ages, as well as less formal observation by parents, teachers and any other carers, such as nursery nurses. In addition, there are special investigations that are made when it is obvious or suspected that all is not well.

FORMAL DEVELOPMENTAL TESTING

Developmental assessments are performed at specific intervals during childhood. They may be carried out by a doctor, health visitor or school nurse. The tests assess physical, emotional and developmental well-being. They also provide an opportunity to give parents information on a variety of topics, including nutrition, sleep problems, immunisations, dental care, and home and road safety.

The height and weight of a child are measured and recorded on special charts. The examiner also measures the circumference of a baby's head. In addition to height and weight, various aspects of development are formally monitored in preschool children, including speech and language, social skills and motor development, which can be viewed in terms of fine motor and gross motor skills.

Charting growth

The pink and blue bands show the range of measurements that are considered normal for the length and weight of a baby girl and boy in the first 12 months of life, as revealed by national (UK) statistics. Plotting an individual baby's height and weight on these charts enables immediate feedback on how a baby Is doing in comparison to others of the same age.

KEY

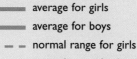

average for girls

average for boys

- - - normal range for girls

- - - normal range for boys

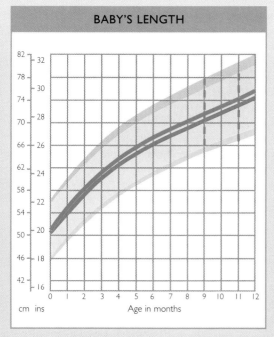

BABY'S LENGTH

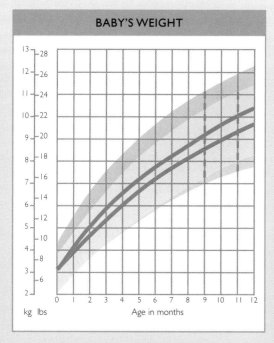

BABY'S WEIGHT

Screening tests for hearing in newborns

Infants with untreated hearing loss are delayed in developing language skills and the ability to understand others, therefore early diagnosis and treatment is very important. Many hospitals are now introducing hearing screening for newborn babies. This is usually carried out using a portable machine brought to the baby's cot. There are two forms of hearing testing for infants: otoacoustic emissions (OAE) and brainstem auditory evoked response (BAER).

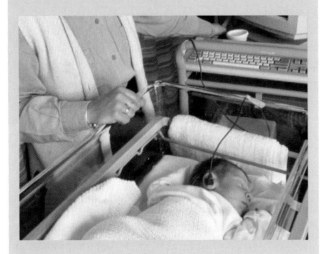

Otoacoustic emissions testing (OAE)

OAE testing (shown here) is slightly simpler and less expensive than BAER and so it is more frequently used for newborn screening. The test picks up the 'noise' made by the sensory cells in the ear that are responsible for hearing. It is performed by putting a small, soft earpiece in the baby's ear and testing the responses received. Testing usually takes only a few minutes per ear. OAE checks out the pathway from the outside of the head to the sensory nerve cells. It cannot differentiate between a non-working sensory cell and a middle ear plugged up because of ear infection. Therefore an abnormal test result does not necessarily indicate that the baby has a hearing disorder.

Brainstem auditory evoked response (BAER)

BAER is a slightly more complex test that is often used as the follow-up test for babies who have not received an 'all-clear' after OAE testing. As with OAE, it detects nerve responses to stimuli. In this case the baby wears headphones that generate specific stimuli, a set of clicks and tone pips, and the nerve response is detected via electrodes attached to the baby's forehead. This testing requires the baby to be relaxed – either sleeping or mildly sedated.

The aim of this monitoring is to check that a child is developing at an appropriate rate and that appropriate developmental 'milestones', such as starting to walk, are occurring. However, it is important to remember that every child is different in terms of personality and to a certain extent patterns of development. Those who monitor child development bear this in mind when making their assessments. Parental concern is regarded as a key indicator and is always taken very seriously.

The following checks are all part of the UK Child Health Surveillance programme.

Newborn check

A newborn baby is given a general examination as well as specific checks, for example to make sure the hips are in their sockets (to exclude hip problems) and to check whether the testes are in the scrotum.

• Congenital hip dislocation (see page 141) requires early orthopaedic treatment to prevent disability in later life.

• If the testicles cannot be felt in the scrotum, it may be that they have become stuck in the abdomen during fetal development and that surgery may be needed in the first year of life to bring them down into the scrotum and fix them there. Without this surgery, the risk of fertility problems and cancer of the testes in adult life may be increased.

Head circumference, vision and movement

a A baby's head circumference is regularly measured. It is expected to grow approximately 12cm (5 inches) in the first year of life. This baby girl is six weeks old.

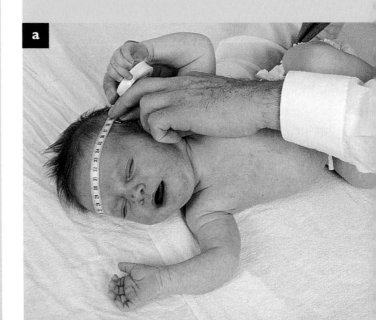

- The eyes are checked for the presence of cataracts (opacities in the lens of the eye).
- Tests are performed on a tiny sample of blood taken from the heel to check for underactivity of the thyroid gland (hypothyroidism) and for phenylketonuria, an inherited disorder that affects the processing of protein (see page 150). Both of these disorders can cause severe learning disabilities and treatment must be started as soon as possible to prevent this and allow normal development.

Six to eight week check

At this age, the baby is checked over, and again the weight and head circumference are measured. The hips and testes are examined again. The doctor looks at how the baby moves; checks the baby's sight by noting whether the baby follows an object moved across its field of vision; and asks the parent about the baby's progress, including whether the baby has started smiling, what noises the baby makes and whether he or she is startled by loud noises.

Six to nine month check

Tests include an assessment of the infant's hearing, and eyes are checked for a squint. Again, movement, language and general behaviour are observed, as well as height, weight and head circumference being recorded.

Later check-ups

Two more assessments are usually performed before a child starts school. Then there is a check-up at the time of starting school, during which vision and hearing are assessed. During the school years, vision and hearing are checked again. These appointments give opportunities for assessment of a child's general health and well-being, plus they offer the opportunity for parents to voice any concerns or questions they may have.

MONITORING LEARNING ABILITIES

As children grow older, teachers play an important part in the monitoring of progress, although clearly the parents still have the central role in this, since they spend most time with the child and have been able to watch the child's progress since birth.

Learning problems may reflect medical, emotional or social problems, or specific learning difficulties such as dyslexia. Parenting problems may also be a factor. When faced with a child who is experiencing problems with learning, a teacher will talk to the child and the parents, and involve the GP if there is a possibility of a medical problem, or in some cases an educational psychologist, who may help in diagnosis and treatment. Sometimes specific learning difficulties are not picked up in early childhood; this may be because a child has managed to hide their problems, perhaps by bad behaviour.

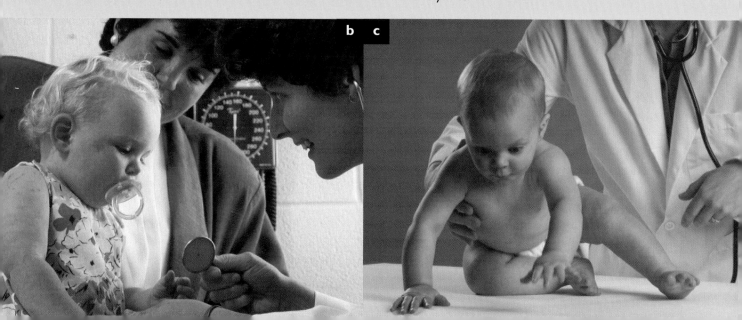

b Vision tests are a key part of developmental checks through infancy and childhood. Here, the baby's attention is caught by the shiny object in the doctor's hand.

c Developing motor skills are also monitored. Here, a doctor watches a nine-month old baby attempting to crawl. Most babies can crawl by this age, although the range of what is considered normal is very wide.

Diagnostic genetic testing

As knowledge of human genetics increases, so does the number of genetic conditions that can be tested for, and the accuracy of this testing. Diagnostic tests are performed to help make or confirm a diagnosis of a genetic disorder where symptoms are already present.

A diagnostic genetic test is carried out to confirm or exclude a diagnosis of a genetically inherited disorder. This is done by direct analysis of the gene responsible. For instance, a child showing delayed growth rates and suffering frequent chest infections may lead the doctor to suspect a diagnosis of cystic fibrosis; the doctor then requests genetic testing to support this diagnosis.

Genetic testing is most often carried out on a blood sample, or sometimes on a cheek swab from the person being tested. Most genetic tests analyse directly the DNA sequence or structure of the gene. These are known as 'molecular' tests or 'molecular genetic analysis'. For some genetic disorders, molecular tests are not the most effective way to confirm a diagnosis. For example, it is simpler to use biochemical genetic testing to confirm diseases such as Tay-Sachs or to analyse haemoglobin (a protein found in red blood cells) in order to confirm diseases such as thalassaemia. However, in these disorders molecular (DNA) tests are still useful once the diagnosis has been confirmed in order to provide carrier testing or prenatal diagnosis for family members of the affected patient.

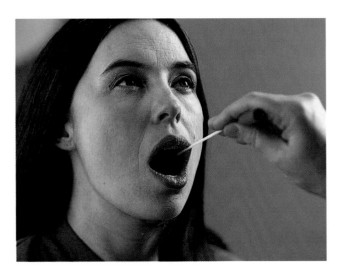

Taking a sample of cheek cells
For molecular testing for a genetic disorder, a good source of DNA is from the cells of the mucous membrane that lines the inner surface of the mouth. The inside of the cheek is rubbed with a cotton swab which is then sent to a laboratory where the testing takes place.

Genetic testing available over the internet

TALKING POINT

Genetic tests are being sold direct to the public over the internet. Conditions for which tests are available include heart disease, asthma and even some cancers. Doctors and organisations such as GeneWatch UK claim that these tests are at the very least misleading and unhelpful. They say that an interview with a doctor or genetic counsellor should be part of every genetic testing procedure. Paternity tests are also available over the internet, using samples such as hairs sent through the post. These tests too have been heavily criticised, not least because they can be done without the knowledge of the mother or child.

DIRECT TESTING

Direct molecular tests seek to characterise the specific genetic defect or 'mutation' in the gene that causes the disease. Mutations are alterations in the DNA sequence that may lead to abnormal proteins being synthesised (or no protein synthesis at all). As a result, metabolic pathways or cellular structures, such as muscle or nerve cells, are disrupted, leading to the disease symptoms. Some changes to the DNA sequence do not affect the gene's protein product. These changes are harmless variants known as 'neutral polymorphisms'.

What the geneticist is looking for
- For some disorders, one specific mutation is common in all affected patients. For example all patients with sickle cell disease have the same haemoglobin gene mutation. These types of mutation are usually very easy to detect.
- For other disorders, such as androgen insensitivity syndrome, all patients have mutations in the same gene, but except for closely related patients, each affected patient has a unique mutation. This means that experts only have to look for mutations in one gene but they

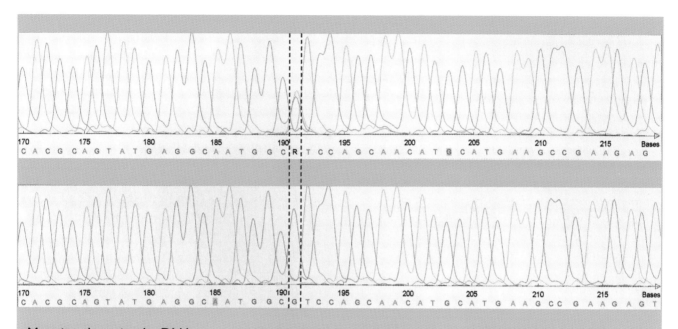

Mutation detection by DNA sequence analysis
Genes are made of DNA, which in turn is made of nucleotide bases. The base sequence of a gene is shown as a series of different coloured peaks and associated letters. Here, the lower panel shows the DNA sequence of a gene from a healthy individual. The upper panel shows DNA from someone with a 'single nucleotide' mutation (highlighted by dotted rules). The healthy person has a G nucleotide in both copies of the gene (one inherited from each parent). The affected patient has a G on the normal allele (gene copy) inherited from his mother but an A on the mutated allele from his father. The sequence analyser identifies the occurrence of A and G bases at this position in the gene with the letter R.

have to analyse the entire gene because the position of the mutation could be anywhere in the DNA sequence.

- Other disorders, such as inherited colorectal cancer, may be caused by a mutation in any one of several different genes. Further, there are no common mutations which means that each possible gene has to be analysed in it's entirety. This analysis is complex and labour intensive, and may take six months or more.

GENETIC VARIATION

Only a fraction of the DNA in the total human genome goes to make up genes. Very large stretches of the genome consists of DNA lying outside of the genes and is called 'non-coding' DNA. Although DNA sequence variations within genes may lead to abnormal protein production (causing genetic diseases), sequence variations in 'non-coding' DNA – called polymorphisms – have no harmful effects. Sequence polymorphisms are inherited in the same way as any other genetic traits and when they are detected by molecular tests, they may be used as 'genetic markers'.

Identity testing for forensic matching

In forensic testing, many different genetic markers from throughout the genome are tested. Results are analysed to estimate the chances that DNA from the crime scene is identical to DNA from a suspect. If one marker does not match, the DNA samples are certain to come from different people. Forensic DNA fingerprinting can never prove with 100 per cent certainty that the two samples are identical, but if a large enough number of markers are tested with no differences seen, the likelihood is very high.

Paternity tests

In paternity testing genetic markers inherited by a child are compared with those in the presumed father (and sometimes in the mother too). As with forensic DNA fingerprinting, one or two unmatched markers can prove the man not to be the biological father. Paternity tests cannot prove with 100 per cent certainty, but a large enough number of matching markers does provide a very high likelihood of true paternity.

Carrier and predictive testing

Carrier and predictive tests detect the presence of a genetic disorder in someone who is not displaying any tell-tale symptoms. Both are used to trace a disease within a family. For some recessive conditions, screening programmes test all members of a population for their carrier status.

CARRIER TESTING

Siblings of a patient with a recessive disease (for example, cystic fibrosis) and sisters of boys affected with an X-linked disease (such as haemophilia) are at risk of being carriers of the disease. A carrier does not experience any symptoms of the disease; instead, the problem is the risk of having affected children. Carrier testing therefore is offered to couples to allow them to make informed decisions when planning a family.

If a couple are both carriers of a disease, there are several ways in which they can avoid the birth of an affected child. They may avoid the risk altogether by not having children, by trying to adopt or by having a child by artificial insemination by an anonymous sperm donor. They could opt for in vitro fertilisation and preimplantation genetic diagnosis. Alternatively, they could choose natural conception and prenatal diagnosis. In cases where prenatal diagnosis indicates that the baby will be affected the couple may opt to terminate the pregnancy or they may opt to continue, in which case they know in advance that their child will be affected and can plan for the future.

PREDICTIVE TESTING

Predictive tests may be taken by healthy relatives of patients affected by dominant adult-onset diseases. Molecular tests are taken before symptoms begin to develop to find out whether the person carries the gene mutation or not – and therefore whether they are likely to develop the disease in the future.

When the disorder is inevitable

Sometimes predictive testing will tell a patient that they will inevitably develop the disorder in question and nothing can be done to prevent it. A prime example is Huntington's disease (HD). This is a devastating neurodegenerative disorder with onset usually in middle age. Predictive testing by direct molecular analysis for the HD gene mutation can be offered. Anyone with a positive genetic test result will know for certain that they will develop HD and also that any children they have will have a one in two chance of also carrying the mutation.

When the outcome is less certain

Huntington's disease is said to be 'fully penetrant' which means that someone who carries the mutation will inevitably develop the disease. Some dominant genes are not fully penetrant. An example is inherited breast cancer. Women who carry mutations in the gene involved have a risk of approximately 75 per cent of developing cancer – the gene is said to have a penetrance of 75 per cent. In this case a predictive test result is less certain. If a molecular test shows the woman to carry the mutation she will have a 75 per cent risk of developing the cancer. Conversely, if the test shows that she does not carry the mutation, she will not develop the inherited form of breast cancer suffered by her affected relatives but she will still be at 'population risk' of coincidentally developing sporadic breast cancer.

For most forms of inherited cancer, there are few lifestyle changes that have any significant impact on the future risk of the disease developing. However, if a

The downside of predictive testing

TALKING POINT

For some people, a predictive test will establish that at some point in the future they will develop an incapacitating, possibly life-threatening disease. Not surprisingly, many people in these circumstances become very upset and depressed. Some would argue that if there are no steps that can be taken to avoid this fate – as is the case with many genetic diseases – what is the point of knowing for certain that it will happen? For some disorders, life insurance and medical insurance is a great deal more expensive for a currently healthy individual with a positive test result. Any individual considering taking a predictive test should receive genetic counselling before and after the test. In the UK, no genetics laboratory will carry out a predictive Huntington's disease test unless pre-test and post-test counselling is being provided.

predictive test result shows someone carries the mutation, they are offered a 'surveillance' programme consisting of frequent medical check-ups with careful examination of organs most likely to develop tumours. This increases the chance of earlier detection and more successful treatment. For some inherited cancers, including breast or colon cancer, patients may opt for surgical removal of part or all of the affected organ before tumours appear, to prevent cancer developing at some point in the future.

METHODS OF CARRIER AND PREDICTIVE TESTING

When a genetic disease has been diagnosed in someone by characterising the genetic mutation, carrier or predictive testing of family members is done by testing the DNA of the family member for the mutation. This is a 'direct' test.

In some families, the genetic mutation is not detectable by direct DNA testing. In these cases, 'indirect' DNA tests may be used instead. Indirect testing involves tracing the inheritance of polymorphic markers through a family. Markers are selected that are known to lie very close on the chromosome to the disease gene in question. If a relative inherits the same pattern of marker alleles as the affected patient, it is very likely that he or she will also have inherited the disease-causing mutation and will therefore be a carrier.

POPULATION SCREENING FOR CARRIERS OF RECESSIVE DISORDERS

A population screening programme involving screening of all members of a population regardless of family history may be used to identify individuals who might be carriers of recessive traits. When screening identifies someone who might be a carrier, diagnostic tests follow to establish whether this is in fact the case. Population screening is useful when a disease carried by autosomal recessive genetic inheritance is common in a certain part of the world or within a particular ethnic group.

Prime examples are:
• **Thalassaemia and sickle cell disease** – thalassaemia in Asians and Mediterranean populations, and sickle cell disease among those of African descent. In both disorders there is an abnormality in the production of haemoglobin. They are screened for simply and cheaply by examining characteristics of the blood cells. If an abnormality is detected on the screening test, direct testing is then carried out to detect mutations present.

The vast majority of all human DNA – 99.9 per cent – is identical from person to person. Only 0.1 per cent is unique to an individual.

• **Tay-Sachs disease** About one in thirty Ashkenazi Jews are carriers of Tay-Sachs. The disease is tested for by a metabolic test looking for the amount of the enzyme hexosaminidase A in white blood cells. Without this enzyme, a fatty substance called GM2 ganglioside accumulates abnormally in cells, especially in nerve cells of the brain, and causes progressive damage to the cells.
• **Cystic fibrosis** This disease has no simple biochemical test and carriers are identified by molecular tests to detect mutations in the cystic fibrosis gene. This gene, called CFTR, is very large, and almost 2000 different mutations have been described. Most of these mutations are very rare. Some however are much more common in certain populations – in both northern Europeans and in Ashkenazi Jews, for example, small number of mutations occur in the majority of carriers. If the carrier test does not find a mutation this does not mean that a person is not a carrier, because the tests cannot detect all the very rare mutations. However, the carrier risk is greatly reduced.

How genetic disorders are inherited

Many – though not all – diseases and disorders with genetic causes are passed on from parent to child. However, parent or child may be a 'carrier' of the disease who will not develop the disorder itself but may pass it on to the next generation as part of their genetic inheritance.

DOMINANT GENES

If a family member carries an abnormal dominant gene, he or she will develop the disorder triggered by this gene. If such a gene is carried, every egg or sperm produced has a one-in-two chance of containing this abnormal gene.

- **Examples of disorders** Huntington's disease, myotonic dystrophy, all forms of familial breast cancer.
- **Chances of a child inheriting the disorder** Each child has a one-in-two chance of being affected.

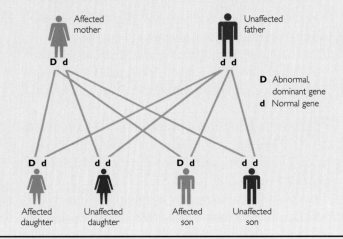

D Abnormal, dominant gene
d Normal gene

RECESSIVE GENES

A single abnormal recessive gene will not affect the mother's or father's health, provided that the matching gene is normal. If a child inherits two copies of the abnormal gene, one from each parent, he or she will be affected. A child who inherits one copy will be a healthy carrier of the disorder.

- **Examples of disorders** Cystic fibrosis, phenylketonuria, sickle-cell disease.
- **Chances of a child inheriting the disorder** Each child has a one-in-four chance of being affected. Each unaffected child has a two-in-three chance of being a carrier.

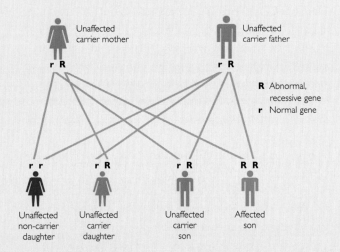

R Abnormal, recessive gene
r Normal gene

X-LINKED GENES

If a woman has an abnormal gene on an X chromosome, she probably will not have the associated disorder because her other X chromosome is likely to carry a normal version of the gene. However, a man carrying an abnormal gene on his X chromosome will have the disorder because (being male) he does not have another X chromosome with a normal version of the gene.

- **Examples of disorders** Colour blindness, Duchenne muscular distrophy, haemophilia.
- **Chances of a child inheriting the disorder** If the mother is a carrier, a daughter has a one-in-two chance of being a carrier; her sons have a one-in-two chance of being affected. If the father is affected, all his daughters will be carriers; his sons will not be affected.

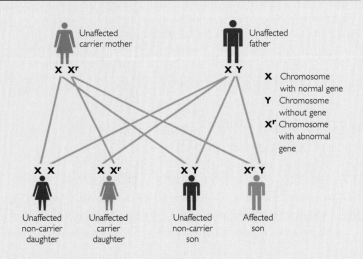

X Chromosome with normal gene
Y Chromosome without gene
X^r Chromosome with abnormal gene

Genetic counselling

Genetic counselling is offered to patients and families who are concerned about the possibility or reality of a genetic disorder. Subjects covered range from the potential effects on future children to the options available for prevention, diagnosis and management of the disease.

Before testing for a genetic disorder takes place, a genetic counsellor, perhaps with another medical professional, will discuss with affected members of the family what tests are available, how they work and the pros and cons of a negative or positive result. After testing, the genetics professional will seek to help family members understand and adjust emotionally to a diagnosis.

They will answer any questions the patient and their family may have on the nature and effects of the disorder, the pattern of inheritance and therefore the likelihood that current or future children may be affected, and what treatments are appropriate and available for the condition.

WHO DOES THE COUNSELLING?

In the UK and USA genetic counselling is generally provided by a medical geneticist, a genetic counsellor or a genetic nurse, depending upon the needs of the individual situation. (See page 97 for further information on these genetic health professionals.) Genetic counsellors and genetic nurses can provide much of the same information as geneticists, but unlike geneticists are not trained to make a diagnosis. Therefore their focus may be less on treatment and more on information provision, psychosocial support and making sure that clients have access to any other relevant specialists, tests and treatment.

TALKING HELPS

Often, clients are referred to a genetic counsellor because they or their doctor think they should explore issues around genetic testing. The genetics health professional does not tell the client what to do, but instead seeks through the counselling process to enable the client to make an informed decision that is right for the client at that time.

Families usually find that talking to a specialist who is familiar with their particular situation is comforting and helpful. A diagnosis of genetic illness may generate strong feelings of guilt or blame – or both – and the input of the counsellor or other genetics health professional can help with this considerably.

All genetic professionals seek to get the best for their clients from the medical system. They also seek to ensure truly informed consent for testing and to follow the testing process through to completion. This involves giving and discussing test results and providing support or referrals to other specialists as needed.

Considering the risks

A genetic counsellor and a doctor talk with prospective parents who might be at risk of passing on a genetic disorder to their children. The counsellor is holding a karyotype – a diagram showing the number and structure of the chromosomes in a single cell. A genetic counsellor often takes part in prenatal counselling when there is a history of inherited disorders in the family.

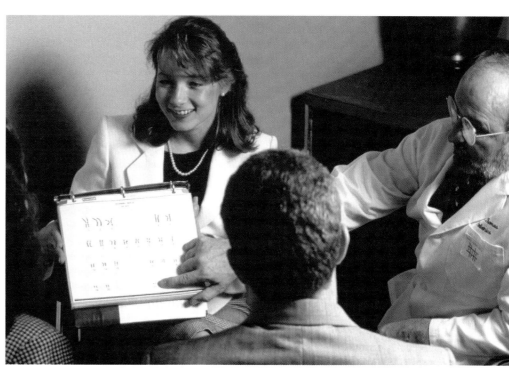

CURRENT TREATMENTS

The year 2000 saw the completion of the human genome project – an international research project to map all our genes. This marked a big step forward in our understanding of how to treat illnesses with a genetic origin, and how to use gene therapies to treat disorders. However, this is just the beginning, and there are many challenges ahead. Diseases and disorders with a genetic cause are particularly complicated to treat because any gene that is at fault is in every single cell of the body.

The following section focuses on the broad range of current approaches to treating different diseases that have a genetic and/or developmental component.

Treatment choices for disorders

The possibilities for treating developmental and genetic problems vary depending on the disorder. Some treatments have a track record of success; others are in their infancy.

When treating an illness, doctors aspire to remove the underlying causes and so cure the condition. With many disorders this is often not possible, and then treatment is targeted at the symptoms.

WHICH TREATMENT OPTIONS ARE BEST?
Having made the diagnosis, doctors and specialists will consider the treatment options with the patient (or the parents of a baby or child). The treatment recommended will depend on a number of factors. Clearly, the patient's wishes (or the parents' wishes if the child is too young) will be a key factor. The doctor will aim to put all the relevant information before the patient so that he or she can make an informed choice. The doctor will also need to consider the patient's general health. For example, surgery may not be appropriate for someone with severe coronary artery disease and other treatment options may be more suitable.

DRUG TREATMENTS
Medication is commonly used to treat illness, but a number of issues need to be considered when a doctor is choosing the most appropriate drug, such as whether there are any existing medical conditions that may be affected by the drug. The doctor will also need to know what other drugs are being taken in case they may interact with the new drug. Potential side effects are an important issue – most prescribed drugs can cause unwanted effects in addition to desired ones. The potential benefits of any drug should outweigh the possible side effects.

HORMONE THERAPIES
Hormonal drugs are prescribed for a variety of reasons. For example, hormone replacement is appropriate when puberty is early or delayed; when the menopause is early; and as a treatment for symptoms of the menopause. Failure to grow caused by a genetic disorder such as pituitary dwarfism may sometimes be treated with human growth hormones.

SURGICAL TREATMENTS

Surgery is an option for some conditions. See page 120 for more information on surgery to repair a birth defect and page 122 for bone marrow and organ transplantation. As already mentioned, surgery may be a problem for patients in poor health. However, increasingly some operations can be performed under local or other forms of anaesthesia in which the patient remains awake. This is making surgery an option for more people.

OTHER TREATMENTS

Other treatment options include physiotherapy, speech therapy and occupational therapy. These have a wide variety of uses, for example regular physiotherapy is used in the treatment of cystic fibrosis. Occupational therapists recommend aids and other measures that can be used in day-to-day living to help patients maximise their potential.

TREATMENT BY DIET

With some conditions, a very specific change in diet has a direct effect on symptoms. For example, with the inherited disorder phenylketonurea (see page 150) treatment involves putting a baby on a diet restricted in the amino acid phenylalanine to prevent the build-up of phenylalanine to toxic levels that cause brain damage.

PSYCHOLOGICAL TREATMENTS

Psychological treatments are not only used specifically to treat mental disorders, they can also target stress and other psychological problems that may contribute to a physical disorder, such as tension headaches or irritable bowel syndromes. Intensive early treatment is a key component in the treatment of many areas of developmental delay.

CHANGES TO LIFESTYLE

For many disorders there are two main aspects to management – medical treatment of the disorder, and measures that the individual can take to relieve the symptoms or reduce the risk factors. A healthy lifestyle has a considerable impact on the symptoms of many diseases and disorders in which there is an inherited predisposition towards the disorder.

For example, a patient with the degenerative disease osteoarthritis can help to relieve symptoms and slow the progress of joint damage by exercising regularly and in a manner that avoids placing undue stress on the affected joints, and by eating sensibly to reduce any excess weight and keep weight stable once a desirable weight is achieved. Someone with coronary artery disease, to take another common example, can do a great deal to help themselves and keep further damage to the coronary arteries to a minimum by not smoking, taking regular exercise (as advised by the doctor), reducing saturated fats in the diet, and losing weight as necessary.

GENE THERAPY

New therapies are emerging that may one day be able to transform the lives of patients affected by many genetic disorders. To cure a genetic disorder, doctors need to understand how the abnormal gene causes the disease and then find a way to sidestep the problem or restore normal function where possible. There is great anticipation that, with the increased information about our genes now available from the human genome project, improved understanding of the pathways of disease will lead to new tailored treatments for many genetic diseases based on gene therapies. For more information on gene therapies, see page 124 onwards.

AT THE LEADING EDGE

Pharmacogenetics

If two people both suffer from, for example, hypertension, it is quite possible that the disorder in each will have a slightly different genetic cause. Therefore, if a certain drug helps to control hypertension by overcoming a specific genetic defect, it will only provide an effective therapy for a patient whose hypertension is caused by that particular defect. The drug will have no beneficial effect for other hypertensive patients who have slightly different genetic defects.

The science of pharmacogenetics (which is still very much in its infancy) aims to gain a much greater understanding of the genetic processes involved. Patients can then be given pharmacogenetic tests to determine which particular defective gene causes their problems, so they can be offered the most appropriate drug to treat their specific defective gene.

Surgery before and after birth

Nowadays, many birth abnormalities can be surgically corrected or alleviated soon after birth – sometimes surgery can be performed before the baby is born. This is, of course, tricky and still at the experimental stage in most cases.

NEONATAL SURGERY

Congenital conditions that are helped by surgery not long after birth include the following:
- cleft lip and palate (see pages 120 and 140)
- club foot (see page 141)
- congenital diaphragmatic hernia
- congenital heart disease (see page 141)
- neural tube defect disorders, of which the most common is spina bifida (see also page 153).

Exactly why these congenital conditions occur is still not known, but there are thought to be both genetic and environmental factors involved.

PRENATAL SURGERY

Sometimes surgeons are able to perform a corrective operation before the baby is born. Prenatal surgery is a new experimental area of treatment and at present only available in a few highly specialist centres (mainly in the USA). Both minimally invasive 'keyhole' techniques and open surgery have been used.

Prenatal surgery is already an option for spina bifida and congenital diaphragmatic hernia. Prenatal surgical procedures at a more experimental stage include:
- surgery on the heart
- surgery for fetal hydrocephalus
- repair of blockages in the fetal urinary tract
- removal of congenital cystic adematoid malformation (a kind of cyst in the fetal lung)
- removal of sacrococcygeal teratoma (a kind of tumour in the lower spine).

SURGERY FOR SPINA BIFIDA

Spina bifida is a relatively common birth defect where part of the spine does not close over properly in the womb and a sac or cyst develops. It affects approximately 1 in 1000 babies.

SOME TYPES OF SPINA BIFIDA

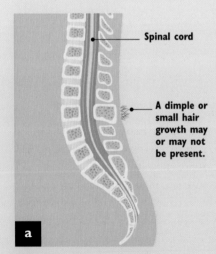

Spinal cord

A dimple or small hair growth may or may not be present.

a

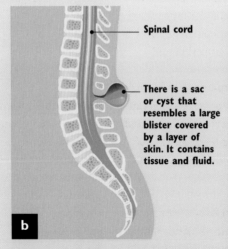

Spinal cord

There is a sac or cyst that resembles a large blister covered by a layer of skin. It contains tissue and fluid.

b

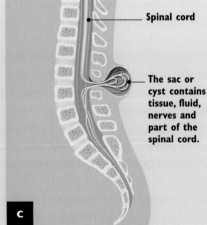

Spinal cord

The sac or cyst contains tissue, fluid, nerves and part of the spinal cord.

c

a Spina bifida occulta (hidden)
In this mild and common form, there is a slight deficiency in the formation of one vertebra (occasionally more than one). It rarely causes disability and sometimes there are no signs or symptoms at all.

b Spina bifida cystica (meningocele)
This is the less common form of cyst-like spina bifida. In this form, there is a sac that contains the tissue which covers the spinal cord and cerebro-spinal fluid. There is usually little disability.

c Spina bifida cystica (myelomeningocele) This is more common than the meningocele form. Damage to the spinal cord causes loss of sensation and paralysis, the amount partly depending on the location of the cyst.

Surgery after birth

Traditionally, the treatment for spina bifida involves surgery to cover the lesion (the sac or cyst) with skin. Any complications are then treated as they arise. Sometimes, when there is the additional complication of too much cerebrospinal fluid accumulating in the ventricles of the brain (hydrocephalus), there may need to be another operation to release fluid pressure in the brain via a ventricular-peritoneal shunt. This is an artificially created overflow system from the ventricles to the abdominal cavity (the peritoneum).

Surgery before birth

In recent years, doctors have begun to suspect that part of the disease process in spina bifida occurs because the open lesion in the fetus is exposed to amniotic fluid, which is poisonous to sensitive nerve cells. This suggests that some of the damage could be averted if the lesion was closed over earlier in the pregnancy and for this reason surgeons have begun to carry out surgery to close the lesion while the fetus is still in the womb, during the second trimester (4–6 months of pregnancy). This is considered to be an experimental procedure and the final data on outcome is not yet available, but most of the babies who had surgery before birth are doing well. There is, however, a risk of prenatal surgery causing early labour and delivery of the baby, and therefore further assessment of the long-term benefits of this surgery is needed to determine whether the risks of an early birth justify the benefits.

OPERATING ON A DIAPHRAGMATIC HERNIA

A congenital diaphragmatic hernia occurs when contents of the abdomen move into the chest cavity through a hole in the diaphragm. The problem crops up in about one in every 2500 births, with the severity of the condition varying greatly. Sometimes the lungs do not have the space to develop properly, and after birth the baby has trouble breathing or cannot breathe at all.

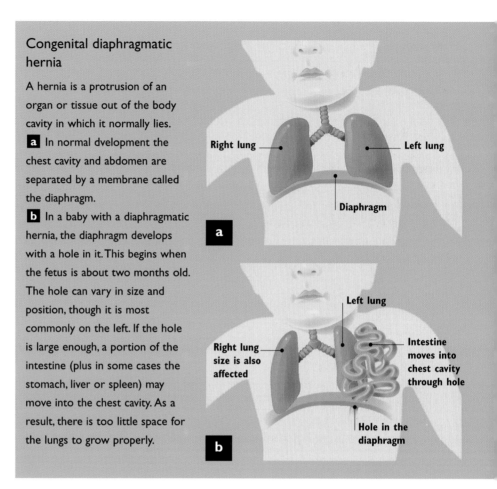

Congenital diaphragmatic hernia

A hernia is a protrusion of an organ or tissue out of the body cavity in which it normally lies.

a In normal dvelopment the chest cavity and abdomen are separated by a membrane called the diaphragm.

b In a baby with a diaphragmatic hernia, the diaphragm develops with a hole in it. This begins when the fetus is about two months old. The hole can vary in size and position, though it is most commonly on the left. If the hole is large enough, a portion of the intestine (plus in some cases the stomach, liver or spleen) may move into the chest cavity. As a result, there is too little space for the lungs to grow properly.

a — Right lung, Left lung, Diaphragm

b — Left lung, Right lung size is also affected, Intestine moves into chest cavity through hole, Hole in the diaphragm

Surgery after birth

The hole can be closed surgically after birth. However, this is not a solution if at the time of birth the lungs are so poorly developed as a result of the hernia that the baby cannot breathe and so cannot survive.

Surgery before birth

Surgeons have tried repairing the hernia prenatally, but this did not appear to improve postnatal outcome and has now been abandoned as a technique.

An alternative technique is a prenatal procedure called fetal tracheal occlusion, in which a clip is placed on the windpipe of the fetus to prevent fluid escaping from the lungs. The idea is that fluid accumulating in the lungs while the baby is in the uterus will help the lungs to expand and grow naturally. Indeed, expansion of the lungs often pushes the abdominal contents that have moved into the chest cavity back into the abdomen. This is still an experimental procedure, but has increased the chances of survival for babies who are severely affected.

Repairing a cleft lip and palate

Clefts of the lip and/or palate occur in about one in 1000 live births. A cleft lip is a congenital deformity of the upper lip which is often accompanied by a cleft palate (a gap in the roof of the mouth). Both can be corrected surgically.

It is not understood exactly why normal fusion of the face fails to occur in babies born with a cleft lip and/or cleft palate. Most forms of cleft lip and palate are thought be caused by a combination of as yet unidentified genetic and environmental factors.

It is usual for clefts of the lip to be repaired when the babies are about 3 months old. Clefts of the palate are generally repaired when babies are between 6 and 12 months of age. Surgery is performed to help with any feeding problems, to achieve as normal an appearance as possible as early as possible, and to minimise the development of speech problems. Surgical repair aims to reconstruct the tissues of the lip and palate, repositioning them in their normal anatomical positions. Repair of a cleft lip involves reconstructing the muscle of the lip and stitching the skin of the lip together. Repair of a cleft palate is achieved by closing the gap in the hard palate and reconstructing the muscle of the soft palate.

Following the initial repair of a cleft lip and palate, speech development is regularly assessed, since a cleft palate can lead to nasal sounding speech which can be be difficult to understand. There is also a possibility of poor growth of the upper jaw or of a bone graft being needed to fill in a gap in the gum.

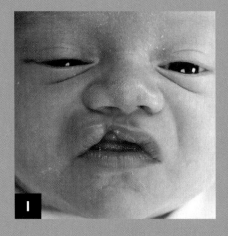

1

1 This baby boy – shown here at a few weeks old – was born with a cleft lip on the right side of his face. (Most unilateral clefts of the lip occur on the left side.) Surgery for the cleft lip is planned for when the baby is three months old.

Preparing for surgery
The baby is given no milk for 6 hours before the operation but is allowed water and clear juice until 2 hours beforehand.

Cleft lip and palate problems

Cleft lip
The various parts of the upper lip fail to join together normally, leaving a gap (cleft) on one side of the lip (as above) or both sides. The cleft lip may affect the shape of the nose.

Cleft palate
Here, the roof of the mouth fails to fuse. The resulting cleft can involve both the hard and soft palate (as above) or just the soft palate at the back of the mouth.

Cleft lip and palate
Sometimes the lip, base of the nose, gums and palate are all affected. The problem may be limited to one side of the mouth (as here) or present on both sides.

This is to reduce the risk of the baby vomiting during the anaesthetic. He is given a sedative by mouth one hour before the general anaesthetic. A tube is inserted into his airway to allow the lungs to be artificially ventilated.

2 A ventilation tube is in place over the middle of the baby's chin, allowing the surgeon clear and symmetrical access to the upper lip. The baby's eyelids are taped shut to protect the eyes. The face is cleaned with antiseptic solution and sterile drapes placed around the face.

3 To aid the surgeon in joining together the related parts on either side of the cleft during the surgical repair, the landmarks of the lip are marked out with surgical ink, together with the planned incision lines.

4 The lip has skin on the outside and mucosa (specialised lining tissue) on the inside, with a circular band of muscle (orbicularis oris) that encircles the mouth in between. The muscle within the lip is separated from the overlying skin and mucosa so that it can be seen as a band of tissue on each side of the cleft.
The tissues of the lip are handled very gently throughout the procedure with skin hooks.

5 The muscle on each side of the cleft is sutured together, bringing the tissues of the lip together into a more normal position.

6 The lip is still a little short on the 'non cleft' (left) side. To correct this, a small triangular flap from the skin of the cleft (right) side of the lip is turned through 90 degrees and inset into a back cut (incision) in the 'non cleft' side of the lip. This lengthens the lip at the site of the lip repair and ensures that the lip looks symmetrical.

7 The skin is sutured.

8 Before the operation, the cleft of the lip distorted the appearance of the nose, but the nose now looks symmetrical.

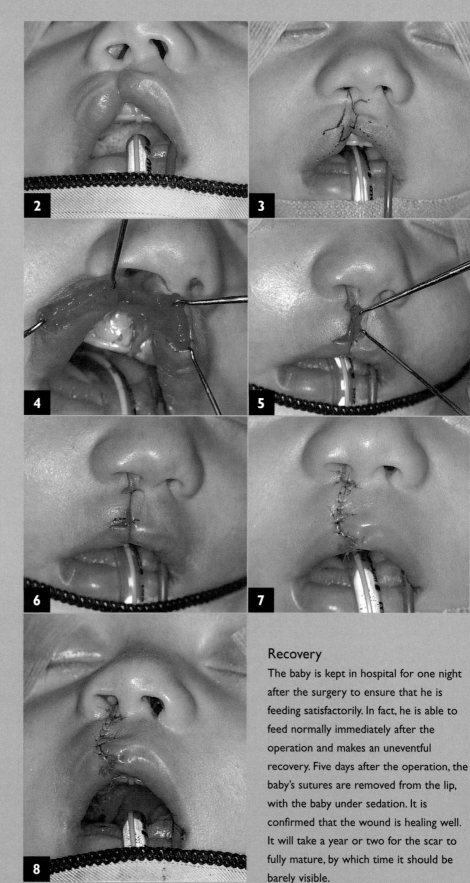

Recovery

The baby is kept in hospital for one night after the surgery to ensure that he is feeding satisfactorily. In fact, he is able to feed normally immediately after the operation and makes an uneventful recovery. Five days after the operation, the baby's sutures are removed from the lip, with the baby under sedation. It is confirmed that the wound is healing well. It will take a year or two for the scar to fully mature, by which time it should be barely visible.

Transplant surgery for genetic disorders

Transplant surgery is one way of compensating for a gene that is not working in a particular organ. There are, however, serious risks of transplant rejection after surgery, and of side effects and risks associated with long-term immunosuppression.

Most cells have signals which normally allow the body to recognise them as self or foreigner. Whenever a transplant is performed, it is important to match the donor and the recipient to ensure that the major signals match. However, it is impossible to completely match all signals unless the material comes from the same individual, and so a regimen of drugs to suppress the immune system are required for the life of the transplant.

BONE MARROW TRANSPLANTATION

Successful bone marrow transplantation was first carried out in the 1980s. Bone marrow is the soft tissue inside the long bones of the legs, arms and ribs. It contains stem cells, which live inside the bone marrow and make a continual supply of fresh red and white blood cells.

Red blood cells are involved in transporting oxygen around the body and contain haemoglobin. When red cells mature they lose their genetic information to make room for as much oxygen as possible. However the white cells, which are part of the immune system, retain their genetic information throughout their natural life.

These cells are responsible for attacking foreign invaders in the body, such as viruses and bacteria.

The theory is that a person with diseased blood cells can be given someone else's healthy bone marrow, which will make healthy red and white blood cells for the recipient. First the recipient's own bone marrow cells are destroyed by irradiation, then the recipient is given a transfusion of healthy bone marrow cells.

Inherited disorders and bone marrow transplantation

Bone marrow transplantation has proved to be an effective treatment for thalassaemia, a hereditary (autosomal recessive) blood disease. This is a rare disorder affecting haemoglobin, the protein that transports oxygen around the body in the red blood cells. The outcome is anaemia that can be mild or very severe.

Bone marrow transplantation is also used to treat Hurler syndrome, a rare hereditary disorder caused by an inability to break down and store sugars properly within the body. Symptoms such as enlargement of the liver and heart defects build up gradually from infancy onwards.

EXPERIENCING A KIDNEY TRANSPLANT

I've known since I was a boy that I have the hereditary disorder Alport's syndrome. In my mid-twenties, my kidneys began to fail and within a couple of years I was on dialysis and needing a kidney transplant. Several members of my family volunteered to donate a kidney and it turned out that my uncle was the best match.

On the day of the surgery, my uncle went into the operating theatre first, where his kidney was removed. Then my operation took place in the

afternoon. The new kidney was transplanted into my abdomen as an addition to my existing kidneys – so now I have three kidneys. The operation took about three hours.

The surgery was carried out through an incision that extended diagonally across my abdomen. Afterwards, the operation site felt tight and painful. I slept a lot, but was encouraged to start moving about as soon as possible, to help the healing process. Two days after the operation I was

able to walk about a little. I was given prescription painkillers, plus anti-rejection drugs.

The new kidney began to work immediately. Regular blood tests monitored how well it was functioning. Just under two weeks after the operation, I was allowed to go home, with strict instructions not to lift anything heavy. A week later I returned as an outpatient to have the staples in my scar removed. Six months later, my new kidney is still functioning well.

Solid organ transplants

As transplant techniques have become more successful, organ transplantation may now sometimes be performed for the following autosomal, X-linked or multifactorial disorders.

Organ	Disorder
KIDNEY	Polycystic kidney disease Alport's syndrome
LIVER	Wilson's disease Biliary atresia
HEART	Congenital heart disease and malformations (many types)
PANCREAS (OFTEN WITH KIDNEY)	Diabetes mellitus type I Pancreatitis
LUNGS (OFTEN WITH HEART)	Cystic fibrosis Pulmonary hypertension
INTESTINE (OFTEN WITH LIVER)	Some congenital intestinal malformations

ORGAN TRANSPLANTS

The transplantation of various body organs is a potential treatment for some genetic disorders. If the disorder is contained within one organ, replacing that organ with a new one can be effective. A lung transplant may be an option for cystic fibrosis, for example. However, in many genetic illnesses, more than one organ is affected, or the gene causing the problem is active throughout the body and transplantation is not an effective cure.

PROBLEMS WITH TRANSPLANTATION

If the transplant is an organ, such as a kidney or the lungs, there is a risk of transplant rejection. The aim is to prevent the recipient's natural immune system from attacking and rejecting the new organ.

If the transplant is of bone marrow, which is a component of the immune system itself, there is not only a risk that the remaining host bone marrow will attack the new transplanted marrow, but there is also a risk that the new immune cells within the new marrow will attack tissues belonging to the host – this is called graft versus host disease.

After transplantation the immune system must be suppressed in order to prevent rejection. This is done with drugs – generally two or three are prescribed that work in combination with each other.

Finding a close enough match

For all transplant recipients it is necessary to find a donor who matches their own tissue type as closely as possible. Matching the donor and recipient requires testing of HLA (human leucocyte antigen) compatibility. This is the comparison of the self versus non-self markers that are genetically determined and present on white blood cells. It is most likely that a match will be found in close relatives, such as a parent or a brother or sister, though sometimes an unrelated donor is discovered. Once an HLA match has been found, other components of the immune system also need to be tested, to reduce still further the chances of rejection.

Tissue compatibility testing

A laboratory technician analyses tissue samples from potential donors and recipients for their compatibility and suitability for organ transplantation. One such test is for HLA (human leucocyte antigen) compatibility.

Gene therapy

Gene therapy is a new treatment for some genetic diseases. It aims to correct a gene that is not functioning properly by removing the malfunctioning gene and replacing it with one that works. The key is to be able to deliver the right gene to the cells that are in need of it.

Gene therapy is still very much at the experimental stage. Only recently has the science of genetics advanced to the point that gene therapy is beginning to become a reality. Scientists disagree when speculating about how great an impact gene therapy might have on the treatment of gene-related illnesses in the future – some are more optimistic than others. All agree that a great deal more research is needed. The first major success story has been the treatment of X-linked severe combined immunodeficiency (SCID), and there are have been extensive gene therapy trials for other genetic diseases, notably haemophilia and cystic fibrosis.

CHALLENGES TO BE OVERCOME

In order to appreciate the work that has already taken place and why gene therapies are becoming available for some disorders but not yet for others, it helps to have some understanding of the problems faced by geneticists.

Understanding what's going on

First of all, scientists must figure out the normal regulation and action of the gene in question, and how

If all the discoveries of the Human Genome Project were to be printed on A4 paper in ordinary-size type, they would fill 750,000 pages.

the gene's malfunction causes the symptoms observed. Genes are the code for proteins, and each specific protein performs a specific role in the body. In order to design a 'cure' for any specific disease scientists need to know how the gene acts normally and how a faulty gene interferes with normal activity to produce signs and symptoms of the related disorder.

Much of the work of the last 15 years at the Human Genome Project has concentrated on learning where genes are and identifying their products. Now, molecular geneticists and biochemists are focusing on interpreting the interactions of the different proteins in a genome and trying to understand how the genes normally work, and how the abnormal gene causes the problems associated with the disorder.

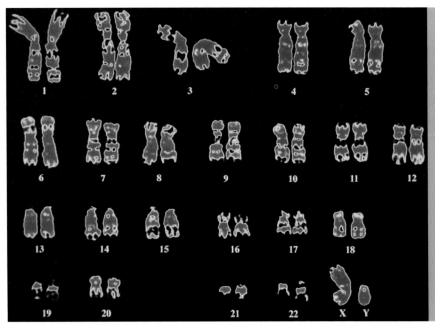

Chromosomes of a human male

Chromosomes carry the genes that determine the characteristics of an individual. In every cell of the human body there are 46 chromosomes, containing a total of around 32,000 genes. The 46 together are called a karyotype. A karyotype is made up of 22 matched pairs of chromosomes and one sex-determining pair (XY in a male, as here; XX in a female). This coloured light micrograph shows the 46 chromosomes of a normal human male. Chromosomes are made up mainly of DNA, some proteins and small amounts of RNA.

Delivering corrected genes to the right location

The first step is to isolate a normal copy of the gene in question from DNA from a healthy individual. Once this has been achieved, it is then necessary to engineer a method to transport the corrected gene not only into the right cell types, but into the nucleus of those cells – the central part of the cell where the all genes are located. And this must be done in such a way that the corrected gene replaces or switches off the faulty gene so that only the new corrected gene is functioning. This has to happen not once but thousands of times, for all the cells that make up the tissue that is affected.

Vehicles to transport the genes

Getting the corrected gene into the right type of cell requires a vehicle to transport it. Scientists have engineered the natural properties of viruses to create gene vehicles, called vectors. Viruses are naturally occurring pathogens that invade cells and manipulate the cell's machinery to make new copies of the virus. Vectors have had the parts of the virus capable of causing disease removed. This leaves room to insert the corrective genes that are to be transported into cells. Different viruses invade different kinds of cells and so are appropriate for different diseases.

An early concern about using modified viruses was that they might still be able to cause illness in the patient. Despite careful genetic engineering to reduce the risk of an immune response in the patient, this has been one of the biggest problems and remains unsolved. The only patient to die directly from experimental gene therapy (rather than from the disease it was aimed to alleviate) had an overwhelming immune reaction to a gene therapy dose delivered in a viral vector.

Another of the big challenges is to find a way to make the vectors function long enough to be effective. Some of the early vectors were quickly disabled by the patient's immune system. Others work well but are too small to carry large genes, such as the muscular dystrophy gene.

In response to these challenges, new kinds of vectors are being developed to insert genes into tissues. One such are liposomes – microscopic lipid 'bubbles' containing the engineered gene; these mimic and fuse with the cell membrane so that the gene is absorbed into the cell. Another are stem cells, which are particularly promising because of their ability to continue to produce new, identical cells – clones of themselves – in the body.

Milestones IN MEDICINE

1988 The Human Genome Project began, with the intention of identifying and mapping the location of all the genes in human DNA. A genome is the entire genetic message of an organism. The project was a massive international research collaboration, coordinated by the US government but including scientists working all over the world.
2000 A first draft of the human genome was achieved.
2003 In April, the Human Genome Project is completed ahead of schedule, to an accuracy of 99.999 per cent. The US National Human Genome Research Institute is now concentrating on increasing our understanding of the role that the human genome plays in health, with the aim of improving diagnosis, treatment and prevention of disease.

Regulation of gene effects

In order to correct genetic disease, scientists also need to know how the genes are regulated, how and when they are switched on and off, or up and down, so that once the genes are in the right place they show the desired activity. Some genes have an effect throughout the life of the organism; other genes are expressed widely during development and then only expressed in specific tissues during normal life. Some genes only need to be expressed in response to particular circumstances. Understanding the regulatory mechanisms and the stimuli for gene expression is important for achieving real 'cures'.

SCID – THE FIRST DISORDER TO BE TREATED BY GENE THERAPY

The famous 'boy in the bubble' was a child with an inherited immune system abnormality called severe combined immunodeficiency (SCID). Patients with SCID do not have normal functioning immune systems to fight off disease-carrying microorganisms such as bacteria and viruses. There are a number of different types of SCID, depending on which white blood cells are affected and why. Without treatment, SCID will prove fatal.

The bubble was a way of providing a sterile environment that protected the patient from infection.

Nowadays, affected children are treated with bone marrow transplantation (see page 122) from healthy donors. However, there are still difficulties in finding matching donors and the possibility of the transplanted bone marrow being rejected or of the transplanted immune cells attacking the treated patient (a disorder called graft versus host disease).

SCID was the first disease to be treated by gene therapy, in the early 1990s. SCID was chosen because the immune cells that are deficient are produced in the bone marrow as white blood cells, and by the beginning of the 1990s bone marrow retrieval and transplantation were no longer considered to be experimental procedures.

Gene therapy trials have taken several different forms. The first trials removed the patient's own bone marrow, manipulated it in order to put in corrective genes and then returned it to the patient.

Another type of trial used donor cells. A third type of trial used cord blood stem cells from fetuses that had been diagnosed prenatally with SCID. One patient treated in this way developed a leukemia-like disease which was eventually attributed to a side effect of the gene therapy. The patient was treated and has since recovered but there remains caution about the potential long-term consequences of using these types of therapies. As a result, gene therapy for SCID is still considered to be an experimental treatment.

GENE THERAPY FOR HAEMOPHILIA

Haemophilia is a rare genetic disorder, in which normal clotting factors in the blood are missing because of mutations in the genes that code for them (see page 146). Haemophilia B occurs because of a deficiency in factor IX; factor IX is secreted into the bloodstream and only a small number of cells need to be secreting factor IX for bleeding to be controlled. Gene therapy experiments, in which a normal copy of the gene is given via intramuscular injection, have enabled the patient's body to produce sufficient factor IX for clotting to take place for as long as ten months. These trials are on-going.

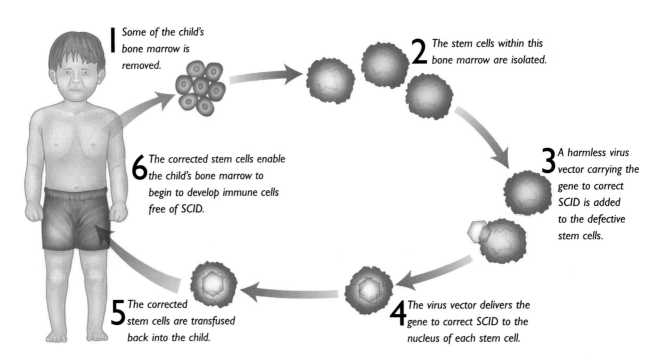

1 Some of the child's bone marrow is removed.

2 The stem cells within this bone marrow are isolated.

3 A harmless virus vector carrying the gene to correct SCID is added to the defective stem cells.

4 The virus vector delivers the gene to correct SCID to the nucleus of each stem cell.

5 The corrected stem cells are transfused back into the child.

6 The corrected stem cells enable the child's bone marrow to begin to develop immune cells free of SCID.

How gene therapy works in treating SCID

First some of the patient's own bone marrow cells are removed, and the stem cells within them are isolated. Next, copies of the corrected gene are transported into these cells, which are then returned to the patient's bone marrow. After this, new blood cells generated from the stem cells within the bone marrow will also contain this corrected gene. As a result, the patient's immune system begins to strengthen and protect the patient from infection.

Cystic fibrosis research
A scientist isolates an artificially produced human protein during laboratory research into gene therapy for cystic fibrosis. He is using a machine that isolates large protein molecules.

GENE THERAPY FOR CYSTIC FIBROSIS

The gene for cystic fibrosis was one of the first to be located and cloned by the new genetic technologies. There were great hopes that this might rapidly pave the way for a genetic 'cure' for this disorder, but these have so far been disappointed. Cystic fibrosis is an inherited disorder which disrupts the normal movement of sodium and chloride across cell membranes. Its effects are seen as thick sticky mucus that affects the lungs and digestive system of patients (see page 142).

Gene therapy has concentrated on trying to introduce a corrective gene into the airways using a variety of vectors. The aim is for the lungs to produce normal mucus rather than the distinctive mucus of cystic fibrosis that is ultimately so damaging to the lungs. Unfortunately, it has proved very difficult to get the gene into the body and functioning for long enough, and in sufficient amounts, to make much difference to a patient's condition. This is after almost 15 years of research. Efforts continue to overcome these difficulties.

OTHER GENE THERAPIES

There are thousands of rare genetic disorders which one day may be candidates for gene therapy, but considerable challenges with delivering genes early enough, in sufficient doses and in a safe manner, hamper progress. One area where gene therapy is beginning to demonstrate clinical applications is in treating acquired diseases, such as cancer and heart disease.

GENE THERAPY FOR CANCER

As scientists' understanding of the genetics of cancer and the development of abnormal cells increases, therapies are being developed that attempt to interfere with developing cancers, by promoting the body's natural immune response or in some other way. Particularly important are therapies designed to increase the effectiveness of p53, a gene involved in the control of cell death that is defective in over half of all cancers. In experimental trials, vectors carrying copies of a normal p53 gene have been injected into tumours. This seems to have slowed the growth of tumours and even induced regression. Research is continuing into possible uses of this therapy.

AT THE LEADING EDGE

Gene therapy and Huntington's disease

A new technique has recently been discovered whereby gene therapy can be used to 'turn off' genes that cause some degenerative diseases, including Huntington's disease, and hopefully stop the disease progressing. The disease process is caused by the presence of an abnormal protein product. The technique to counteract this uses a cell's natural ability to switch off genes as a defence against viruses. Short segments of DNA introduced into the cell trigger chemicals to hunt for any other DNA with the same sequence and destroy the templates used to create the damaging protein. This essentially turns off production of the abnormal protein. These techniques have shown promise in animal experiments. No human trials have yet been carried out but there is great excitement that this may be breakthrough treatment.

Stem cell research

Stem cell research is an experimental and controversial field of medicine that may one day revolutionise many areas of health care. Before these dreams can come true, however, there are important ethical issues that must be resolved.

Accidents, injuries, degenerative diseases and simple old age can damage or destroy almost any part of the machinery of the body. Unlike a man-made machine, however, the human body can rarely be repaired by simply replacing the damaged or worn-out parts, because the immune system recognises replacements as foreign tissue and attacks them, leading to 'rejection'. Transplant recipients have to take high doses of immunosuppressant drugs that leave them vulnerable to disease and are only partially effective, and there is a massive shortage of donor organs and tissues anyway.

But what if you could have replacement tissues specifically grown to match your body so perfectly that the immune system would welcome them? This is the dream of stem cell therapy, an exciting field at the cutting edge of medical technology, which could help to cure anything from cancer and heart failure to spinal injury and Alzheimer's disease.

EXPLAINING STEM CELLS

Most of the cells in the body are descended from stem cells, non-specialised cells that have the power to give rise to different types of cell. When a stem cell divides, its daughter cells can follow one of a number of developmental pathways. The many different types of blood cell, for instance, develop from haematopoietic stem cells that live in the bone marrow.

Ultimately all cells trace their ancestry back to the cells that made up the embryo – the least specialised cells of all. A single cell taken from an embryo that is just a few days old has the potential to develop into any type of cell in the human body, depending on the chemical signals that it receives.

In stem cell therapy the aim is to use such cells to grow tissues and organs that the body will recognise as 'self'.

STEM CELL POTENTIAL

The marvellous versatility of stem cells could be put to many different uses.

- **Growing new bone marrow or body tissues** Bone marrow transplant is the main treatment for blood diseases, such as leukaemia. Success rates would be greatly improved if stem cells could be used to create replacement bone marrow free of disease. One day it may be possible for someone with heart disease, say, to have stem cells grow fresh, healthy heart tissue that could be implanted without fear of rejection.

- **Conditions affecting the nervous system** Because nerve cells do not ordinarily divide in an adult it is almost impossible to regrow severed spinal cords or replace disappearing or defective brain cells. But if neural stem cells could be cultured it would be possible to grow new nerve cells to graft into damaged spines, benefiting paraplegics like the actor Christopher Reeve who is

Stem cells from embryos – right or wrong?

Before stem cell therapy can become a reality scientists need to research such factors as how to control the development of the stem cells to produce the tissues that are needed. But to do this requires stem cells, and currently the main source of these cells is from embryos left over after in vitro fertilisation. The embryos are destroyed in the process. Antiabortionists say that this is wrong. But there has been intensive lobbying in support of stem cell research from many patient groups (some represented by celebrity advocates such as Christopher Reeve, right). Stem cell research using embryos is currently allowed in the UK, Sweden, Finland, Greece and Holland, and in the USA. It is illegal in France, Germany, Spain and Ireland and blocked in several other EU countries.

Stem cell therapy using an embryo

If stem cells were to be harvested from an embryo and used to treat a disease, as might happen in the future, this would be the likely sequence of steps.

1 An egg cell is fertilised by a sperm cell. (Neither egg nor sperm needs to be from the patient to be treated.)

2 to **4** The resulting embryo divides three times in the next three days.

5 By day five the embryo consists of a mass of stem cells and an outer layer that will form the placenta.

6 The stem cells are removed and cultured, making the embryo non-viable.

7 Different tissue types may be grown, such as brain tissue, heart tissue or skin.

8 For example, heart muscle cells may be grown from the stem cells and then injected into a heart to treat disease.

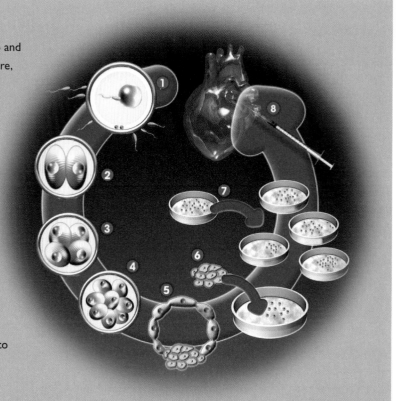

understandably a leading exponent of stem cell research. Growing new brain cells from a patient's own tissue could also make brain grafts a routine treatment for disorders such as Parkinson's and Alzheimer's disease.

• **A longer life** The ability to grow new body parts or tissues to order could also make rejuvenation technology a reality. Our bodies could be replaced piecemeal as they wore out.

STEM CELLS FROM CORD BLOOD

Stem cells are present in the 'cord blood' in the umbilical cord of a newborn baby. Some scientists have suggested that these stem cells should be taken and frozen so they can be used to treat the baby in later life, if necessary. However, other scientists are sceptical as to whether this would work. Also, using stem cells in cord blood is only an option for those whose cord blood has been saved.

Creating a baby who could donate stem cells

A way round this problem is for close relatives (generally the parents) of the person needing stem cell therapy to conceive a baby who after birth can donate stem cells from the umbilical cord that are a close enough genetic match to the person needing the stem cells.

For example, in cases of devastating blood disorders such as Diamond Blackfan Anaemia (DBA), the only cure is bone marrow transplants from a donor who is a close enough genetic match to the recipient for the immune system to be fooled. If a close enough match cannot be found, an alternative is for the patient's parents to conceive in the hope that the resulting child will not have the condition but will be a close enough match to be a donor. Stem cells can then be extracted from this baby's umbilical cord and used to treat the patient with the disorder.

Using IVF (in vitro fertilisation) technology, it would be possible to create several embryos and then use genetic screening to select only those that are disease-free and a perfect match.

At the moment this approach is not permitted by the UK's Human Fertilisation and Embryology Authority, because of concerns that it is unethical to conceive a child primarily so that its organs or tissues may be harvested (and obviously without its consent). The technique is allowed in the USA, however, and in a much-publicised case in 2003, parents of a DBA-afflicted son went to the US to conceive another boy with compatible stem cells.

Cloning and genetic modification

Scientists speculate that one day we will be able to use cloning technology in order to grow replacement body tissues or even create an 'identical twin'. Additionally, genetic modification may be able to prevent genetic diseases or enhance such traits as athletic ability.

NATURAL BORN CLONES

A clone is an organism that is genetically identical to another organism. Creatures that reproduce asexually, such as aphids, produce clones, as do plants that reproduce by sending out runners, such as strawberries. Human clones already exist in the form of identical twins – two people who developed from the same fertilised egg and are therefore genetically identical. 'Identical' twins show that clones may not grow up to be exact duplicates of one another, whatever their genes, because they are physically and mentally different.

CREATING A CLONE

Several species of mammal, including sheep, cows and mice, have now been cloned. This is achieved by taking the nucleus from a cell belonging to the animal to be cloned and implanting it in a egg cell from which the nucleus has been removed. The enucleated egg can come from any female animal of the same species. It is an empty egg with no genes of its own and therefore is genetically quite separate from the nucleus that it harbours as part of the cloning process. The clone offspring will be identical to the donor (male or female) from which the nucleus was taken.

Is human genetic enhancement a good idea?

If scientists become able to genetically modify human embryos for desirable mental and physical characteristics, where should the line be drawn in terms of what traits can and can't be selected? Many argue that it would be OK to use genetic engineering to ensure a baby will not suffer from a life-threatening or crippling genetic disease. But how about genetic disorders that are not so severe? Where do you draw the line? And who makes the decision – the parents, the doctor or the state? What should be legal and what should be illegal? A lot of issues will have to be addressed that have never needed to be considered before.

The cell created by combining nucleus and egg cell then divides several times over – the first stage in the development of an embryo that is the clone of the animal who donated the nucleus. If it is to develop further, the embryo must gestate within a uterus. Therefore the embryo is implanted in the uterus of a surrogate mother. The surrogate mother could be any female animal of the same species. Neither enucleated egg nor surrogate mother

The world's first cloned horse
This foal, named Prometea, is genetically identical to her 'mother', effectively making them identical twins. Prometea was born in Italy in May 2003. She was created when scientists fused a skin cell with an enucleated egg from another horse. Scientists then implanted the activated egg in the uterus of the mare who had donated the skin cell.

Some scientists hope that in the future genetic manipulation may increase our expected lifespan by decades. Already, researchers in Italy have successfully genetically modified mice to increase their lifespan by a quarter.

contribute genetic material to the clone – they are simply a means of enabling the fetal development and birth of the cloned animal.

Problems with the cloning process

At the moment, many cloned embryos must be created to achieve a single viable adult animal Another major problem is that research shows that clones are more vulnerable to congenital defects, weak immune systems and subsequent health problems, and consequently have shortened lifespans. For instance, Dolly the sheep, the first mammal ever to be cloned successfully in the way described above, died of a lung disease in 2003 at the age of six – half her natural expected lifespan.

CREATING A HUMAN CLONE

Theoretically, it could one day be possible to clone a human being. However, human cloning is a controversial issue that raises many ethical considerations. There are also major technical hurdles that lead most genetics experts to say that human cloning is not currently possible. In most countries the attempted cloning of human beings is either against the law or likely to become so in the near future.

Why clone a human being?

Even though cloning seems to be difficult and dangerous, there are potential reasons why humans might want to produce clones of themselves.

Therapeutic cloning

The cells of a cloned embryo could be used as stem cells for stem cell therapies for the 'parent' with no risk of the stem cells being rejected by the parent's immune system. This would do away with the need for the patient to take immunosuppressive drugs, and experience the long-term side effects of these drugs.

The cloned embryo would be allowed to divide only a few times, after which the embryonic stem cells would be collected and used to grow genetically matched tissues or specific cell types – or even organ replacements – needed to treat the 'parent'.

A way of having a child

For men or women who do not produce viable sperm or eggs, a clone might one day offer the chance to conceive a child bearing their own genetic material.

A key step in genetic modification

The ability to clone an embryo a number of times over is seen by a few scientists as an essential requirement for any future genetic enhancement of human beings. This is because the techniques of genetic engineering are so tricky that the speculation is that it will be unlikely that a desired genetic modification will be achieved at the first attempt. Hence a number of identical embryos are needed.

GENETIC ENGINEERING OF A HUMAN

Such is the risk of unwanted complications that genetic engineering is not regarded by scientists as safe to use on human beings, and none has taken place. However, there has been a great deal of speculation on what the future might hold. Areas of potential genetic enhancement might include, for example, the prevention of specific diseases, or the improvement of stamina and strength.

It is thought by some that scientists might be able to achieve human genetic modification by the following method. A single cell is taken from a week-old embryo, then one or more genes are added, deleted or modified. The cell is placed inside an egg from which the nucleus has been removed, and the resulting embryo is implanted in a woman who may or may not be the biological mother. The embryo will grow into a genetically engineered child.

IT'S NOT TRUE!

'Cloning is the key to eternal life'

The notion of creating a clone to achieve immortality is pure science fiction. A cloned baby would grow up to be a different person with a different personality and consciousness, and would have no way of sharing the memories of his or her 'parent'.

Living with a long-term disorder

With many long-term conditions, it is possible to live a normal or near-normal life. With other disorders, health problems may be much more severe and potentially disabling. However, similar strategies for coping often apply, whatever the severity of the problems.

Long-term disorders may be non-genetic or genetic in origin. Chronic genetic disorders are sometimes obvious at or soon after birth, or first show symptoms during childhood, or are what is sometimes described as 'late onset', meaning that symptoms develop later on in life.

For all long-term disorders, regardless of origin, treatments are generally a matter of management and alleviation of symptoms, rather than cure.

THE DIAGNOSIS

When first faced with the diagnosis of long-term disease, it is often difficult to take in all the information given by the doctor. Therefore, it is important to take time to consider the diagnosis and to return to the doctor if necessary to find out more. (Research shows that people remember on average as little as 10 per cent of what they have been told by a doctor.)

It may be worth the patient noting down questions in advance and talking to a close relative or friend; these measures may help to clarify the situation in the patient's

mind. However, in many conditions, such as osteoarthritis (joint damage caused by wear-and-tear), the symptoms develop gradually, giving more of an opportunity to come to terms with the condition.

TAKING CONTROL

Understanding the condition can help an individual to feel more in control of the situation and to make more informed decisions. The patient should be aware of the possible treatment options and discuss them fully with the doctor. This will help to ensure the patient feels satisfied with the treatment being offered.

It is important to remember that no treatment programme is set in stone and that the situation will need to be reviewed at intervals to take account of any changes. It is also important to understand what treatment is being prescribed and why, as well as any important side effects that may occur in the case of drugs being taken. With some chronic conditions, such as asthma, the symptoms tend to flare up intermittently. The individual needs to know the plan to be followed in these circumstances and when to seek medical help.

THE IMPORTANCE OF SUPPORT

It is also helpful if partners, close relatives or friends of the patient understand the condition. This will help them to provide the appropriate support, both emotional and, where necessary, practical.

For certain conditions, it is important to know what to do in emergency situations. For example, in cases of epilepsy it is best if someone close knows the steps to follow if the person has a convulsion; or in cases of diabetes mellitus, what to do if a hypoglycaemic episode occurs (this is when the blood sugar level falls to a very low level).

Practical help for those whose activities are limited may not only include shopping and helping with the washing but may also need to take account of the social side of life – perhaps accompanying the individual to the cinema or just dropping in for a chat. For many, being able to confide in family and close friends is a great comfort.

WHERE TO GET HELP

Some people with chronic diseases may be entitled to particular benefits or other help. It is important to find out whether you are entitled to any special help.

- **Local support groups and national associations** are available for a wide range of chronic conditions. They can offer invaluable advice and support on every aspect of a disease. This is not only important for those affected but also for relatives and friends who are carers.
- **Specialist nurses** also work in some disease areas and can provide a wealth of information.
- **Free prescriptions** are available to patients with some chronic illnesses, such as asthma.
- **Disabled parking** may be available to you if you have impaired mobility. In addition, there may be reduced or free travel on public transport.

As well as following the medically prescribed treatment programme, it is important for anyone with a long-term disorder to consider what they can do themselves to alleviate symptoms and improve general well-being.

DIET
Following a healthy diet and maintaining a reasonable body weight is crucial. Not eating properly can undermine any other treatment or self-help strategies. 'Eating properly' includes, for example, ensuring there are no deficiencies in the diet, such as calcium, and keeping a check on intake of fatty foods that can cause high blood cholesterol levels and associated disorders.

EXERCISE
Regular exercise is very important. It is both pleasurable and beneficial, helping to build up strength, suppleness and stamina. Exercise is possible even when mobility is limited. Many people with osteoarthritis, for example, still benefit greatly from gentle exercise, and particularly swimming, which exercises muscles while water supports the body.

MENTAL ACTIVITY
Maintaining interests and developing new ones exercises the mind, maintains purpose and keeps spirits up. Activities may vary from embarking on an educational course to following sport on television, to doing the crossword every day, to learning a language.

REST AND RELAXATION
Pacing yourself and taking time out on a regular basis is as important as any other self-help strategy. Stress and anxiety accompany the majority of chronic conditions; this needs to be acknowledged and the appropriate steps taken to counteract their effects.

DEALING WITH PROBLEMS

Various problems will be encountered by people with chronic conditions. With many diseases and disorders, it may be possible to continue a normal or near-normal life. With other conditions, there may be mild limitation of activities or more severe disability that prevents an individual from continuing his or her job. For some people, stress and anxiety are more of a problem than the physical limitations.

Limitation of movement

With time, someone with mobility problems comes to know what can or cannot be achieved, and will adjust their life accordingly. This can be a difficult process, however, and one that needs the support and understanding of those around them.

Sometimes, mobility problems are not visibly obvious. For example, some people with coronary artery disease may find that their activities are limited to a certain extent – there may be a limit to how far they can walk before they experience chest pain, for instance. In such cases, it is a good idea to seek medical advice on which activities and forms of exercise are beneficial in the circumstances and which should be avoided.

Those who have more obvious limited mobility and/or problems with dexterity also need advice on maximising what they can do. Occupational therapists, and some national organisations, advise on aids and other measures that help with the activities of daily living. Talking to

other people with the condition is another invaluable source of ideas. In some cases, it may not be possible to pursue an existing job but alternatives may be available.

Pain and discomfort

As well as prescribed medication, it may be worth considering other avenues that may help to relieve pain, such as massage, for example.

Psychological problems

People with chronic mental disorders may experience a variety of associated problems, such as memory impairment, that can affect activities of everyday life every bit as much as can physical problems. Support and advice from the GP, the mental health care team and support groups is key to dealing with such problems.

Problems with public perception

This is unfortunately associated with a number of chronic conditions, in particular some mental disorders. The fact that the negative attitude of some people generally results from a lack of understanding is little comfort. Support from those who see the individual rather than the illness is an important part of dealing with this and as medical knowledge increases, it is to be hoped that fear and prejudice will recede.

Fear and uncertainty

These may accompany many conditions. Getting a firm grasp on what the condition is, taking an active role in planning treatment and voicing fears, either to medical workers, as part of a support group or through counselling can all help in dealing with these feelings.

SPECIFIC TO GENETIC DISORDERS

Those who wish to have children but suspect they may be at risk of passing on a genetic disorder may decide to seek genetic counselling and information on the tests available. Those who already have children may need advice on the risks of their children being affected, and on tests.

Down's syndrome
This developmental disorder arises from a chromosomal abnormality. The range of intelligence among individuals with Down's syndrome is very wide, with some Down's children able to benefit from mainstream schooling and later on, as adults, hold down a job and earn their own living.

A TO Z

OF DISEASES AND DISORDERS

This section gives information on the main illnesses and medical conditions that have genetic causes, and disorders in which both environmental and genetic factors are important. The entries are arranged alphabetically and each is structured in a similar way:

What are the causes?

What are the symptoms?

How is it diagnosed?

What are the treatment options?

What is the outlook?

ACHONDROPLASIA
A genetic disorder in which the bones fail to grow normally, resulting in short stature.

What are the causes?
The condition results from a gene defect, which may be inherited in an autosomal dominant manner or may arise spontaneously; this is known as a 'new mutation'.

What are the symptoms?
The trunk is normal length but the limbs are short. There is a characteristic head shape, with the upper part of the skull being large and the face being relatively small. There is sometimes curvature of the spine and affected individuals tend to have a waddling gait. The condition is occasionally associated with hydrocephalus, an accumulation of fluid in the brain. Intelligence is usually within the normal range.

How is it diagnosed?
The diagnosis is usually apparent at birth but becomes clear as a child grows. It is possible to test for the gene abnormality directly. Achondroplasia may also be diagnosed prenatally by ultrasound scanning.

What are the treatment options?
Treatment is not usually needed, although surgery may be needed to relieve hydrocephalus, if present.

What is the outlook?
Life expectancy is usually normal. Some affected adults have back problems due to the curvature of the spine.

ALBINISM
An inherited lack of pigmentation in the skin, hair and eyes.

The main skin pigment is melanin, without which the skin is pale with a pinkish tinge, the result of blood flowing through it. However, the term albinism covers a group of disorders, since the degree of pigmentation lack varies between individuals. In some cases, the eyes are mainly affected and the skin and hair colour are normal.

What are the causes?
Many cases of albinism result from a defect in production of an enzyme called tyrosinase, which helps the body to convert the amino acid tyrosine into melanin.

Most types of albinism are inherited in an autosomal recessive manner; an individual must have two copies of the abnormal gene to have the disorder. If one of the two copies of the gene is normal, pigmentation is normal and the individual is a carrier.

What are the symptoms?
The skin and hair are often very pale; the hair may appear white or very pale blond. The eye colour of affected individuals varies from pinkish to pale blue and even brown, depending on the amount of pigment present.

Eye symptoms vary in severity between individuals and may include:
- rapid jerky movements of the eyes backwards and forwards (called nystagmus);
- a squint;
- sensitivity to bright light;
- visual impairment, including near or long-sightedness.

How is it diagnosed?
The condition is usually diagnosed from the appearance of the individual and the eye symptoms. A test may be performed to look for the missing enzyme. Since the disorder can result from a variety of gene abnormalities it may be difficult to pick up carriers by gene analysis.

What are the treatment options?
Measures may be needed to help with the eye problems, such as glasses to improve vision and sunglasses to protect the eyes from bright light. Optical aids, such as magnifying glasses and small telescopes, may also be recommended.

Affected individuals need to use appropriate sun-screening creams to protect their skin.

What is the outlook?
The outlook is good; people with albinism have a normal life expectancy. However, some people with the condition develop psychological problems related to society's reaction to their appearance.

ALPORT'S SYNDROME
An inherited condition characterised by progressive deafness and renal failure.

Men who are affected usually develop nephritis (inflammation of the kidneys) leading to end-stage renal failure. Women with Alport's syndrome are in the main less affected than men – only one in ten women experiences renal failure to the point of needing dialysis.

What are the causes?
This genetic disorder may be autosomal dominant, X-linked dominant, or (less commonly) autosomal recessive. The gene mutations that occur vary from family to family and this may be reflected in the varying severity of symptoms.

What are the symptoms?
There is usually high-frequency hearing loss which gets progressively worse. Blood in the urine, high blood pressure, and protein in the urine may all become evident. Ultimately the individual suffers end-stage kidney failure.

How is it diagnosed?
Hearing problems are usually obvious, but may be so mild that only special tests detect them. Blood in the urine is sometimes visible in children, but in adults is generally only detectable by a laboratory. Protein in the urine may show up as swelling in the lower legs. Blood tests may reveal abnormalities in kidney function.

What are the treatment options?
When the disease has progressed to the point that the patient has chronic renal failure, dialysis and then kidney transplantation come into play.

What is the outlook?
With the introduction of dialysis and kidney transplantation, the outlook is much improved. The rate at which kidney function deteriorates varies. Patients, generally men, are usually in early adulthood – in their twenties, thirties or perhaps older – before they need dialysis.

ALZHEIMER'S DISEASE
The most common form of dementia, Alzheimer's impairs brain function, affecting memory, intellectual functioning and personality.

What are the causes?
Many factors may play a role in the development of Alzheimer's disease. The condition sometimes runs in families, suggesting that gene abnormalities are involved. In Alzheimer's, the number of nerve cells (neurons) in the brain is reduced and abnormal protein is deposited.

What are the symptoms?
The condition comes on gradually, with a deterioration in memory, especially short-term memory, problems with understanding and working things out, together with moodiness and emotional outbursts, and often depression.

How is it diagnosed?
It is usually diagnosed by talking to the individual and family members. This may be followed by a formal assessment of intellectual functioning. Tests may be arranged to exclude other causes of dementia, such as recurrent strokes.

What are the treatment options?
Drugs may be appropriate in some cases. Where the disease is mild or only moderately severe, they may slow the progress of the disease and may even provide improvement in some cases. Drugs may also be prescribed for certain

Can I be tested for susceptibility to Alzheimer's?

Evaluation of a potential genetic test is underway in the USA. It is based on the apolipoprotein E (ApoE) gene, one variation of which – ApoE4 – is much more common in Alzheimer's sufferers over the age of 65 than in those of the same age who do not have the disease. However, there are many people with Alzheimer's who do not have the gene, and some over-80s have the gene but have not developed Alzheimer's. Doctors and scientists are cautious about advising asymptomatic individuals to have the test, noting that it could cause unnecessary distress with an individual perhaps wrongly attributing a momentary lapse of memory to the onset of dementia, when there is no certainty that a person with the ApoE4 gene will go on to develop the condition. For those who wish to have the test, counselling and support are vital.

However, testing may be useful as a diagnostic tool in patients who are showing symptoms. It may also help researchers who are looking at delaying onset of the disease: by recruiting volunteers, they can identify those who are susceptible and monitor them for signs of deterioration. Estimates suggest that delaying the onset of Alzheimer's by five years will reduce by 50 per cent the number of people suffering from the condition.

ASK THE EXPERT

features of the disease, such as agitation and depression. Support for both the affected individual and the carer is an important part of the treatment plan.

What is the outlook?
Alzheimer's is a progressive disease, but it may be possible to slow the development in some cases and also to relieve some of the symptoms.

ASTHMA
A chronic condition characterised by intermittent episodes of wheezing and shortness of breath of varying severity.

Asthma may be allergic and associated with other allergic conditions such as eczema and allergic rhinitis. Allergic asthma can run in families, suggesting genes may play a role. Different family members may develop different allergic conditions.

What are the causes?
In asthma, the airways become inflamed and narrowed, resulting in breathing problems. Asthma symptoms may result from an allergic response to various substances, including house dust mites, animal dander – the protein found in pet skin flakes and saliva – and pollen. Sometimes there is no obvious cause. Asthma may also be triggered by a viral illness affecting the respiratory tract, often a cold. In some instances, symptoms may be triggered by exercise or worsened by stress.

In addition, asthma may be brought on by certain substances in the workplace, such as glues. The condition is worsened by smoking.

What are the symptoms?
The main symptoms include wheezing, shortness of breath, tightness in the chest and a cough. Sometimes, coughing is the main symptom. If an attack is very severe, the wheezing may no longer be heard, there may be difficulty speaking and eventually there may be blueness of the tongue and lips due to a lack of oxygen.

How is it diagnosed?
The diagnosis can often be made from a description of the symptoms. The doctor may ask the individual to blow into a peak flow meter, which records the maximum rate at which a person can exhale and this may also help in

making the diagnosis. The doctor may also arrange lung function tests, which make a more detailed assessment of breathing. Once on treatment, individuals may be asked to keep a diary of their peak flow measurements; this helps in the assessment of asthma control.

What are the treatment options?
Inhaled reliever drugs are the mainstay of treatment. However, all except those with very mild symptoms also use inhaled preventer drugs, in particular corticosteroids.

Reliever drugs (short-acting bronchodilators), such as salbutamol, are mainly used to ease symptoms when they occur by relaxing the muscles in the airway walls. They begin to have an effect within minutes and last for a few hours. Preventer drugs, such as corticosteroids and longer-acting bronchodilators, aim to prevent attacks. Corticosteroids relieve the inflammation in the airway lining. Long-acting bronchodilators are similar to salbutamol but their effects can last for up to 12 hours.

What is the outlook?
The severity of asthma varies. A number of different treatments are now available, which means that the condition can be adequately controlled in most people.

ATHEROSCLEROSIS
A common condition of ageing in which the arteries become narrowed due to fatty deposits on their lining.

Atherosclerosis may cause a variety of conditions, including coronary artery disease (the blood vessels supplying the heart are affected), strokes (the vessels supplying the brain are involved) and peripheral vascular disease, in which the blood vessels supplying the limbs are narrowed.

What are the causes?
Certain factors predispose people to the development of these fatty deposits. They include smoking, diabetes, high blood pressure and high blood cholesterol levels.

What are the symptoms?
These depend on the affected arteries. Coronary artery disease may result in chest pain (angina) or, if an artery becomes blocked, in a heart attack. Pain in the calves when walking is usually the first sign that the blood supply to the legs is impaired. Various symptoms may be caused by a stroke, depending on which part of the brain is affected.

How is it diagnosed?

The condition is often diagnosed when symptoms, such as chest pain, occur and are investigated. However, in some cases it is found during a medical check-up, for example if the pulses in the legs cannot be felt or if evidence of angina is found on a heart tracing during an exercise electrocardiogram to monitor the heart's electrical activity under stress by exercise.

What are the treatment options?

Measures should be taken that aim to slow or possibly halt the progress of the disease. These include stopping smoking; eating a low fat diet (and taking lipid-lowering drugs); and taking action to lower raised blood pressure, such as exercise and medication. Medication is often needed to relieve the symptoms caused or reduce the risk of tissue damage. In some cases, surgery may be performed to reduce or bypass the narrowing in an artery.

What is the outlook?

The progress of the disease can be slowed by diet and lifestyle modification, but in cases of stroke or heart attack, the damage may cause permanent impairment or disability.

CANCERS

Malignant tumours caused by the overgrowth of cancer cells in the body.

Cancer can occur in the body's various organs and tissues, such as the breasts, bowel and lungs; it can also affect the blood, when it is known as leukaemia. Eventually, the original tumour (the primary cancer) may spread to other parts of the body through the circulatory and lymphatic systems to form secondary tumours, or metastases.

What are the causes?

In most cases, cancer is a multifactorial disorder. Environmental and lifestyle factors cause genetic mutations which trigger the growth of cancer cells. Examples of such factors that sometimes cause cancer to develop include excessive exposure to ultraviolet rays in sunlight, and being a smoker.

In some cases (approximately one in twenty) the disease runs within a family, suggesting inherited genetic factors are involved. In certain types of breast cancer, for example, genes responsible for increasing risk have been identified. Indicators of a genetic predisposition include:

- several family members with the same cancer;
- several family members with cancers that may be genetically associated, such as cancers of the breast and ovary, or of the bowel and endometrium (uterus lining);
- two relatives with the same rare cancer.

What are the symptoms?

These vary depending on the site of the cancer and whether it has spread.

How is it diagnosed?

The diagnosis may be made when tests are arranged to investigate certain symptoms. These may include blood tests, X-rays and imaging tests, such as ultrasound, computed tomography (CT) scanning or magnetic resonance imaging (MRI).

Other possible investigations include those in which viewing instruments are passed into hollow organs of the body, such as the gut (endoscopy), the bladder (cystoscopy) and the lungs (bronchoscopy). The inside of the abdomen can also be viewed during laparoscopy. Biopsies of the affected areas are taken wherever possible to confirm the diagnosis and to identify the cell type involved. This will help to guide the specialist in the most appropriate treatment.

Cancer, and even some precancerous changes may, be picked up during screening (for example, a mammogram or cervical smear), but further tests will be needed to confirm the diagnosis.

Tests may also be arranged to look for evidence of the spread of the cancer to nearby lymph nodes and to other parts of the body.

What are the treatment options?

Various treatments are available; they are chosen on the basis of a number of factors, including the type of cancer and whether metastases are present. These treatments may aim to cure the disease, slow its progress or relieve symptoms. The main types of treatment are surgery, radiotherapy, chemotherapy, hormone treatments and biological therapies.

Surgery may be curative in some cases, when the aim is to remove the tumour and surrounding tissue so that the cancer will not spread in the future. Alternatively, surgery may be used to relieve symptoms.

Radiotherapy and chemotherapy both aim to destroy cancer cells. Hormone therapy is used to treat certain cancers. For example, in some cases of breast cancer,

What is the genetic link with breast cancer?

Alterations in the BRCA 1 gene on chromosome 17 has been linked to the development of breast and ovarian cancer, as have mutations in the BRCA 2 gene on chromosome 13. Genetic testing can demonstrate whether a woman (or possibly a man in the case of breast cancer) carries the mutated gene, and may be offered to women with a strong family history of the disease. Genetic counselling is recommended before and after testing. However, an altered BRCA 1 gene does not necessarily mean that a woman will develop breast cancer: up to 25 per cent of women who carry the defective gene never develop the disease. Furthermore, this gene is thought to be responsible for only 5 per cent of cases of breast cancer – the rest arise spontaneously. The benefits of testing are to end uncertainty in people who are at risk because of confirmed family history. A positive result can prompt more vigilance and more frequent mammograms (leading to early detection and more successful treatment); the information with which alert relatives; and perhaps to make choices over childbearing. The downside is mainly psychological: a positive result can be alarming, a negative one may induce feelings of guilt if other family members test positive.

ASK THE EXPERT

growth of the tumour is under the control of the female hormone oestrogen. The action of this hormone can be blocked by the anti-oestrogen drug tamoxifen.

New cancer treatments include the so-called biological therapies, a term used to describe a variety of agents used in the treatment of cancer or in the relief of treatment side effects to repair, stimulate or enhance the immune system.

Some treatments, such as painkillers, have no effect on the cancer itself but rather aim to relieve the symptoms caused by the cancer or its treatment.

In future it may be possible to treat certain cancers with gene therapy.

What is the outlook?
This depends on the type of cancer and whether it has spread to other parts of the body. For some types the outlook is good, especially if the cancer is diagnosed early and treatment is started promptly.

CLEFT LIP AND PALATE
A split in the upper lip and the roof of the mouth which is present at birth.

What are the causes?
During fetal development, several structures come together and fuse to form the face and mouth. If this process is not completed, a cleft lip and/or a cleft palate may be present.

These conditions sometimes run in families, although often there is no family history.

What are the symptoms?
Both conditions vary in severity between individuals. A cleft lip may consist of a notch in the lip, or may extend up towards the nose or into the nose itself. Cleft lips may be unilateral, affecting only one side, or bilateral, affecting both sides.

If a cleft palate is present, there is a connection between the mouth and the nose. A cleft palate may affect only the soft palate at the back of the roof of the mouth or may extend into the hard palate that lies in front of the soft palate. Babies with a cleft palate may have problems feeding. Some of them have hearing problems associated with 'glue ear', in which fluid accumulates in the middle ear. Sometimes the positioning of the teeth is affected.

Cleft lip doesn't usually cause problems with speech. Cleft palate may affect the production of sounds, sometimes giving them a nasal tone.

How is it diagnosed?
The diagnosis is made from the physical examination.

What are the treatment options?
Babies with a cleft palate may need special help with feeding. Often bottle feeding is better; mothers can express breast milk to be given by bottle and special teats are available. Surgery for a cleft palate depends on the nature of the abnormality. More than one operation may be needed to rearrange the tissues (pp. 120–21).

Cleft lip repair is often performed by the age of about three months. Additional surgery may be needed later – for cleft lip to improve the appearance, and for cleft palate to improve the production of speech.

As well as surgery, speech and language therapy, monitoring of hearing and orthodontic treatment when permanent teeth come through may be needed.

Genetic counselling may be offered to advise on the risk of having another affected child.

What is the outlook?

Overall, the prognosis is likely to be good with the surgical techniques now available. However, the outcome depends on the extent and severity of the cleft.

CLUB FOOT

A congenital abnormality of the positioning of one or both feet. Also known as talipes.

In this condition, the foot usually points inwards and downwards. Less commonly, it points outwards or upwards.

What are the causes?

The cause is uncertain. The condition runs in families in about a quarter of cases, suggesting a genetic link, although the responsible gene has not been identified in humans. The condition may also be environmental: doctors suggest uterine 'crowding' may contribute. The risk of having a second affected baby is quite small.

How is it diagnosed?

The condition can be diagnosed prenatally by ultrasound scanning but is more likely to be noticed at birth.

What are the treatment options?

Conservative treatment is often tried first and may involve strapping or using splints to force the foot into position (sometimes a plaster cast is used) and physiotherapy.

Surgery is needed if conservative measures are unsuccessful. The most common method is to lengthen the ligaments and tendons to allow the foot to assume a normal position, which is then maintained for a period by a plaster cast.

What is the outlook?

The prognosis is generally good, although regular reviews may be needed because the problem may recur and require further treatment.

COLOUR BLINDNESS

A condition in which various colours are confused with one another.

What are the causes?

About 8 per cent of boys and 0.5 per cent of girls are born with a disorder of colour vision. Most colour blindness is X-linked recessive in origin. Women are carriers and the daughter of a colour-blind man will always be a carrier. However, a disorder of colour vision may develop as a result of damage to the retina or optic nerve.

What are the symptoms?

Ninety-nine per cent of all cases involve either weak red vision (protanomaly) or weak green vision (deuteranomaly). Rarely, someone may have a problem centred around the colour blue (tritanopia).

How is it diagnosed?

Colour blindness is diagnosed by means of tests that involve looking at coloured pictures or plates. For example, the Ishihara test has coloured numbers or patterns set against a different coloured background; someone with a colour vision disorder will see a different number to someone with normal vision.

What are the treatment options?

Specially tinted glasses may help some people to distinguish colours that they are liable to confuse.

CONGENITAL DISLOCATION OF THE HIP (CDH)

A condition present from birth in which the end of the femur does not lie in the hip socket (the acetabulum) as it should.

Usually, the head, or upper end, of the femur sits securely in the acetabulum, the cup-shaped socket of the pelvis. In some babies, however, the hip is dislocated and lies outside the acetabulum or is dislocatable, which means that certain movements displace the ball from the socket.

What are the causes?

CDH may be caused by poor development of the acetabulum, which means that the head of the femur can slip out of position. There is sometimes a family history, and a breech delivery, in which a baby is not born head first as it should be, increases the risk.

What are the symptoms?

There are usually no obvious symptoms in babies. Sometimes their posture is affected. Problems with movement and walking will emerge later if the condition is not picked up.

How is it diagnosed?

The condition is usually picked up during the hip check, which is performed when a baby is 6 weeks old and then again at 6–9 months. Ultrasound scanning will be arranged to confirm the diagnosis.

What are the treatment options?

The hip is held in position by a splint for 3 months. This allows the acetabulum to develop normally. If this treatment is unsuccessful, surgery may be needed.

What is the outlook?

The prognosis is good with treatment. If the disorder is not diagnosed, a permanent limp or abnormal gait will develop.

CONGENITAL HEART DISEASE
Structural abnormalities of the heart that are present at birth.

Various such abnormalities can be present. Examples include atrial and ventricular septal defects; these are holes in the wall that separates the upper and lower chambers of the heart respectively. Other possible defects include stenosis, or narrowing, of certain heart valves. In some cases, a combination of abnormalities is present.

What are the causes?

These defects arise when the normal development of the heart is disrupted. The reasons why this occurs are often unknown, although both genetic and environmental factors may play a role. Rubella infection in the mother during pregnancy can be associated with heart defects. Babies with Down's syndrome have an increased risk of heart problems.

What are the symptoms?

These vary according to the abnormality, but may include:
- Breathlessness due to heart failure (when the heart is too weak to pump blood around the body effectively).
- Cyanosis, noticed as blueness of the lips and tongue.
- Failure to thrive.
- Some affected individuals are at risk of endocarditis (inflammation of the heart lining due to infections that may enter the bloodstream during dental procedures).

How is it diagnosed?

Defects may be diagnosed prenatally during the detailed ultrasound scan carried out at around 20 weeks gestation.

Alternatively, a heart murmur (the noise created by disrupted blood flow through an abnormal valve and heard through a stethoscope) may be noticed during a routine baby check.

The abnormality will usually be diagnosed by echocardiography, a form of ultrasound that assesses the structure of the heart, and Doppler ultrasound, which assesses the flow of blood through the heart.

What are the treatment options?

Treatment may involve drugs for heart failure and surgery to correct or minimise the effects of the abnormality. Surgery is often carried out during the first year of life.

Measures are taken to reduce the risk of endocarditis, including antibiotics before dental treatment and certain types of surgery, and thorough dental hygiene to prevent plaque build up.

What is the outlook?

This is likely to be good when surgery is performed for the more simple abnormalities. However, more complex abnormalities may be less amenable to surgery and so the individual's activities may be restricted.

CYSTIC FIBROSIS
A genetic disorder in which abnormally thick secretions are produced by certain organs, impairing their function.

The thick secretions block the smaller airways of the lungs and increase the risk of infection, making lung infections common. Thick secretions also block channels in the pancreas, causing damage. Male fertility is often impaired. There are also excessive amounts of salt in the sweat.

What are the causes?

The condition results from gene defects on chromosome 7 and is inherited in an autosomal recessive manner. In families who have a child with cystic fibrosis, each parent is a carrier. Each child conceived by the parents will have a one in four chance of inheriting cystic fibrosis, and a two in four chance of being an unaffected carrier like the parents.

What are the symptoms?

Common features include:
- Persistent cough producing excessive amounts of sputum and wheezing.
- Frequent greasy stools.

- Poor weight gain with impaired growth. This is because the pancreas cannot produce digestive juices as it should, so the absorption of food in the gut is impaired.

Some affected babies are born with a blockage of the gut. In adolescents and adults there may be a deficiency of insulin resulting in high blood glucose levels.

How is it diagnosed?

A sample of sweat is analysed for its salt content. DNA analysis may also be performed.

In most cases, carriers can be identified by gene analysis. Genetic counselling is offered to affected families.

What are the treatment options?

Frequent chest physiotherapy is needed, with postural drainage, a method for clearing excess secretions. This must be performed several times a day. Prompt treatment with antibiotics is necessary to treat lung infections as they arise. Pancreatic enzyme supplements are needed and a special high-protein, high-calorie diet is required, as well as vitamin supplements.

Cystic fibrosis is most common in Caucasians with 1 in 25 people being carriers. This falls to 1 in 65 in Afro-Caribbeans and 1 in 90 Asians.

A lung transplant may be considered in cases where lung damage is severe.

Experiments are ongoing into the use of gene therapy to treat cystic fibrosis, with the aim of one day offering those affected the chance of a normal life without drugs.

What is the outlook?

This prognosis has improved over recent years, thanks to the treatments available. Affected individuals born after 1990 have a good chance of reaching the age of about 40.

DIABETES MELLITUS

A disorder in which blood sugar levels are persistently raised, which can cause a variety of complications in both the short and long term.

Insulin is needed to help the cells absorb glucose from the blood, as well as to stop the liver producing glucose.

What are the causes?

In type I diabetes, the pancreas does not produce insulin, or produces insufficient. In type II diabetes the main problem is a failure of the cells to respond to insulin; sometimes there is also a lack of insulin.

Type I diabetes tends to develop earlier in life than type II which is usually considered to be a disease of middle and old age. However, obesity is a risk factor for type II diabetes, and as obesity is on the increase in children as well as adults in many Western countries, type II diabetes is increasingly affecting younger age groups, including teenagers.

Genetic factors are thought to play a role in both types. In type I diabetes, the body produces antibodies against the pancreas for unknown reasons. Sometimes diabetes mellitus is caused by another disease, such as chronic pancreatitis (long-term inflammation of the pancreas).

What are the symptoms?

The typical symptoms of diabetes mellitus are thirst and passing urine frequently. However, these are not always present, and in type II diabetes the symptoms may come on very gradually and be more vague. In fact, there may be no obvious symptoms, and type II diabetes may only be noticed during a routine check-up if a urine sample is analysed for the presence of sugar.

Hypoglycaemia, in which the blood sugar falls to a low level, may occur, particularly in those with type I diabetes when treated with insulin. People with diabetes and their relatives and friends need to know how to recognise a hypoglycaemic episode and what to do when this occurs.

Another serious condition called ketoacidosis may arise in type I diabetes if sugar control is disturbed. Sugar levels in the blood become very high and toxic substances called ketones accumulate, requiring urgent treatment.

Diabetes increases the risk of a number of diseases, such as coronary artery disease, eye disease, strokes and peripheral vascular disease, in which the blood vessels supplying the limbs become narrowed. It may also be associated with kidney disease and peripheral neuropathy, in which the nerves supplying the body are damaged, causing a variety of symptoms including tingling and numbness of the feet.

How is it diagnosed?

The disease may be picked up by a routine urine check. It is usually confirmed by measuring blood glucose levels. Blood sugar needs to be carefully monitored from then on and regular check-ups are needed to look for complications, as well as to assess blood sugar control.

What are the treatment options?

Type II diabetes is usually treated by drugs, which increase the sensitivity of the cells to the effects of insulin and/or increase insulin production.

Patients with type I diabetes use insulin injected under the skin. The doses given may need to be altered from time to time to meet the body's changing needs.

What is the outlook?
People with diabetes mellitus are at risk of various complications both in the long and short term. The aim of treatment is to achieve the best blood sugar control possible and so to reduce these risks.

DOWN'S SYNDROME
A condition arising from a chromosomal abnormality, in which three copies of chromosome 21 are present rather than the usual two.

This syndrome is characterised by certain physical features and learning disability, and may be associated with a number of complications.

What are the causes?
In Down's syndrome, cells contain three copies of chromosome 21, rather than the usual two. The extra chromosome is usually inherited from the mother, and the likelihood of this happening increases with maternal age.

What are the symptoms?
There are certain characteristic facial features, such as a broad flat face with a short nose and slanting eyes. The head may be small, and the tongue may be prominent. The hands and feet tend to be short and wide with a single skin crease across the palm. Affected individuals are usually small for their age.

Congenital heart disease is common, affecting around 40 per cent of children with Down's syndrome. There may also be abnormalities in the structure of the bowel.

Hearing problems may occur due to glue ear, in which there is a build up of fluid in the middle ear. There may be delays in development, although individuals often develop very well socially.

There may be an increased risk of certain diseases, such as hypothyroidism and leukaemia.

How is it diagnosed?
Pregnant women are offered a blood test – the maternal serum test – that identifies those at an increased risk of having a baby with Down's syndrome. Measuring the nuchal thickness (the thickness of the skin at the back of the neck) during an ultrasound scan at around 11 weeks may also be used to assess the risk. Amniocentesis produces a definitive diagnosis by direct analysis of the chromosomes in the sample taken.

Individuals with Down's syndrome are often identified by their appearance. The diagnosis can be confirmed by chromosomal analysis. Once a diagnosis is made, the heart is assessed for structural abnormalities. Genetic counselling is offered to the family.

What are the treatment options?
These children are carefully monitored. For example, their hearing and thyroid function are regularly assessed. Problems, such as glue ear, are treated if they arise. Surgical treatment to correct heart and bowel abnormalities is performed where possible.

Affected children can often go to a mainstream school if arrangements can be made there to meet their special needs.

What is the outlook?
The intellectual ability in Down's syndrome varies between individuals, but most lead happy and rewarding lives. Life expectancy varies depending upon the associated complications, such as congenital heart disease, but many individuals with Down's syndrome live into middle age and in some cases longer.

DUCHENNE MUSCULAR DYSTROPHY
A genetic disorder that causes a progressive weakness and wasting of muscles.

What are the causes?
The disorder is caused by a gene abnormality found on the X chromosome. Boys who have the abnormality suffer from the disease and girls who have a copy of the abnormal gene are carriers (girls have a normal copy of the gene on their other X chromosome which compensates). Becker's muscular dystrophy is also an X-linked recessive condition. It produces similar symptoms to Duchenne's but they begin later and the condition develops more slowly.

What are the symptoms?
Symptoms usually become apparent at around the age of three, when the child has difficulty in running because of weakness in the pelvic muscles. Difficulty climbing stairs and a waddling gait develop. The muscles of the calves are enlarged but weak. Later, weakness of the arms develops.

Eventually, boys with the condition need to use a wheelchair. Their breathing muscles become affected and lung infections occur.

How is it diagnosed?
The blood levels of a substance called creatinine kinase are elevated. The doctor may take a muscle biopsy; if the disease is present, the muscle will show characteristic changes. It is also possible to diagnose the condition prenatally by DNA analysis where there is a family history.

What are the treatment options?
Physiotherapy is needed to maintain as much mobility as possible. Research is being carried out into the use of some corticosteroid drugs which can offer temporary relief from muscle weakness. Support is needed for the affected individual and for his family. The family will also be offered genetic counselling.

What is the outlook?
The disease cannot be cured, and the condition tends to be fatal in the twenties.

FRAGILE X SYNDROME
The most common inherited cause of learning difficulty, predominantly in males and a leading cause of autism.

What are the causes?
Fragile X is transmitted genetically on the X chromosome. Men pass the defect on to their daughters, but not their sons; the child of a mother who is a carrier has a 50 per cent chance of inheriting the gene. The area of DNA on which the gene sits varies in length from one person to another, but in some people it becomes excessively long, a change known as a 'premutation'. People with the premutation may not have symptoms of fragile X but when the gene is handed down it may elongate much further, effectively switching off the gene. Males are more severely affected than females because they have only one copy of the X chromosome: in females only one active copy of the X chromosome is needed, so the defective gene may be deactivated in many tissues leading to milder symptoms.

What are the symptoms?
Symptoms include:
• reduced mental function, with varying degrees of learning disabilities;

• difficulties paying attention;
• hyperactivity;
• anxiety;
• autism;
• long face, large ears, flat feet and elongated fingers.
Intellectually, boys are more severely affected, although both boys and girls with the syndrome suffer from emotional and behavioural difficulties.

How is it diagnosed?
The condition may be suspected in a child with developmental delay or behavioural problems, but is confirmed by DNA testing; the test also detects carriers.

What are the treatment options?
Educational intervention and medication can help many children, but sufferers are affected for life.

What is the outlook?
There is currently no cure for fragile X. However, researchers believe that the FMRP protein for which the affected gene codes delays, rather than destroys, the development of connections in the brain. Treatments being developed aimed at normalising these connections should be of potential benefit.

Fragile X affects up to 1 in 3500 males and 1 in 8000 females of all races. One woman in 250 and one man in 800 are carriers.

FRIEDREICH'S ATAXIA
A progressive disorder in which damage to nerve tissue results in weakening and wasting of muscles.

What are the causes?
This condition results from an abnormality on chromosome 9, which is inherited in an autosomal recessive manner.

What are the symptoms?
The symptoms usually begin between the ages of 8 and 16. Difficulty in walking is associated with unsteadiness and slurred speech. Curvature of the spine may be a feature, as well as a number of heart problems, including hypertrophic cardiomyopathy, in which the heart muscle is thickened but is unable to pump blood around the body efficiently.

How is it diagnosed?
The condition is usually recognised from the symptoms and an examination.

A genetic test may be performed to look for the abnormal gene. Tests may also be arranged to measure the electrical activity in muscles and the speed at which impulses travel along nerves. An echocardiogram may be performed to examine the heart.

What are the treatment options?
Currently no treatment is available for the disease itself. Treatment aims to relieve the symptoms; for example, drugs may be prescribed for heart disease, and physiotherapy and special aids provided to help with mobility.

What is the outlook?
People with the condition may live until the age of about 40. However, life expectancy varies between individuals, depending on several factors, including whether they have heart disease.

HAEMOPHILIA
A genetic condition that causes a deficiency of one of two proteins needed for clotting of the blood.

For blood to clot, a complex series of processes must occur involving a number of proteins called clotting factors.

What are the causes?
In haemophilia A, the most common type of the disease, there is a lack of clotting factor VIII; in haemophilia B, factor IX is lacking. The genes responsible are found on the X chromosome and are inherited in a sex-linked recessive manner. This means that only boys can actually have the condition and that only girls can be carriers, passing on the abnormal gene to their sons. However, although girl carriers have a normal copy of the chromosome which compensates for the abnormal gene, some of them still have lower levels of the clotting factor than normal and may have the features of mild haemophilia.

In some cases, haemophilia arises with no previous family history of the condition due to a new mutation in the gene involved.

What are the symptoms?
The symptoms of the two types of haemophilia are the same, but haemophilia B is less common. The severity of the conditions varies, depending on the degree of the deficiency. In very severe cases, where there is virtually none of one of the factors present, bleeding occurs spontaneously. With less severe cases, increasing degrees of physical trauma are needed to cause bleeding to occur.

In the more severe cases, pain can occur due to bleeding into muscles and joints (in particular the elbows, knees and ankles). Eventually, without treatment, joint damage and arthritis can develop.

How is it diagnosed?
The more severe cases tend to be identified from around the age of six months because easy bruising tends to be noticed as children start to move around. Mild cases may not be noticed until later. If the condition is suspected, the clotting of the blood is assessed and then the factor levels are measured. Where there is a confirmed family history, it is now possible to diagnose the condition during pregnancy and to test women to see whether they are carriers.

What are the treatment options?
Treatment mainly consists of replacement of the deficient factor by intravenous injections. In moderate and severe cases, this treatment is usually given regularly, with the aim of preventing abnormal bleeding occurring; in such cases it is also given when bleeding occurs. For mild cases, the injections are given when needed to prevent prolonged bleeding following surgery and injuries.

Haemophilia and the royal families of Europe

TALKING POINT

The most famous example of a family to have suffered from the inherited illness haemophilia is undoubtedly that of Queen Victoria. The gene mutation for haemophilia within the royal family is thought to have originated spontaneously with Victoria. Of her nine children, her son Leopold suffered from the disease – he died from a haemorrhage after a fall at the age of 31 – and her daughters Alice and Beatrice were carriers. Alice's daughter Alexandra, who married Tsar Nicholas II, was also a carrier, passing the condition to their only son Alexis. Alexandra's misplaced conviction that the 'mad monk' and charismatic healer Rasputin could cure her son was a contributing factor to the deep unpopularity of the Russian imperial family before the Russian Revolution of 1917. From Queen Victoria, haemophilia also spread to the royal families of Spain and Germany.

Those affected are advised to rest the area where bleeding has taken place. Genetic counselling is offered where appropriate.

What is the outlook?
The prognosis is much improved, thanks to the treatments now available. These largely prevent the joint damage and arthritis that were problems in the past.

HEREDITARY HAEMOCHROMATOSIS
A genetic disorder in which the body absorbs too much iron from the diet. This then accumulates in various organs of the body and causes damage.

Iron is needed to make red blood cells. However, in this condition excessive amounts accumulate, mainly in the liver but also in other parts of the body, such as the pancreas, heart, joints and glands that produce hormones.

What are the causes?
The condition is caused by a gene defect inherited in an autosomal recessive manner. Haemochromatosis may also occur secondary to another disorder.

What are the symptoms?
Men are more likely to have the disorder and suffer from it at an earlier age, as women regularly lose iron during menstruation and use stores in pregnancy. The following features may be present:
• persistent tiredness;
• joint pains;
• impotence and loss of libido;
• bronzing of the skin.
Diabetes mellitus may develop, as well as disease of the heart muscle resulting in heart failure, because the heart is unable to pump blood around the body effectively resulting in breathlessness. There is a risk of cirrhosis (permanent liver damage) and as with other types of cirrhosis, the risk of liver cancer may be increased.

How is it diagnosed?
Blood tests are performed to look for evidence of iron overload. A DNA test to locate the abnormal HFE gene confirms the diagnosis in 95 per cent of cases.

What are the treatment options?
Treatment consists of the weekly removal of blood. The body then uses some of its iron stores to make more red blood cells. Once blood tests confirm that the excessive iron has been used up (this may take around two years or even longer), the procedure will be required less frequently, perhaps three or four times a year for life, to keep the situation under control.

What is the outlook?
Treatment should be started as early as possible, with the aim of avoiding complications such as cirrhosis and diabetes mellitus. If treatment is started early and the iron overload is not too severe, the prognosis is good and life expectancy is likely to be normal.

Hereditary haemochromatosis is the most common single gene disorder in Caucasians, with 1 in 10 being carriers.

HIGH BLOOD PRESSURE
A common condition, also known as hypertension, in which the pressure of the blood in the arteries is raised.

Blood pressure is defined in terms of two figures: the systolic pressure (the upper figure) represents the pressure in the arteries when the heart contracts to pump blood around the body, and the diastolic figure (the lower figure) corresponds to the pressure in the arteries between the contractions. Average blood pressure is around 120/80 but the level accepted as normal varies: a higher level may be deemed normal in an elderly person. In general, blood pressure that is consistently 140/90 or less is acceptable.

High blood pressure that is persistently raised can cause damage to organs such as the eyes and kidneys, as well as increasing the risk of strokes and coronary artery disease.

What are the causes?
A genetic susceptibility is thought to play a role in many cases of high blood pressure. Blood pressure is also affected by lifestyle: the risk is increased by being overweight, drinking excess alcohol, stress and a high salt intake. The likelihood of high blood pressure also increases with age.

Usually, a specific cause is not identified (this is known as essential, or primary hypertension), but in some cases the condition arises due to another medical problem, for example, kidney disease.

What are the symptoms?
Having high blood pressure does not usually cause any symptoms. If it is very high, however, there may be associated headaches, blurred vision and nose bleeds.

How is it diagnosed?

The blood pressure is monitored on several occasions before treatment is considered. The back of the eyes (the retinae) may be examined, using a viewing instrument called an opthalmoscope, to check for any damage. In addition, blood tests may be arranged, for instance to look for evidence of kidney damage.

What are the treatment options?

Lifestyle changes may be sufficient to bring mildly elevated blood pressure back to an acceptable level.

If the blood pressure remains elevated, drugs will be recommended, sometimes diuretics in the first instance and various antihypertensives. These drugs lower blood pressure by reducing the force of heart contractions and by dilating blood vessels. Taking a small dose of aspirin every day may also be recommended for those with high blood pressure who are particularly at risk of having a stroke or developing coronary artery disease. (This should be taken only on a doctor's advice, since it is not suitable for everyone.)

What is the outlook?

With the wide variety of treatments now available, it should be possible to bring blood pressure under control and so reduce the elevated risks of strokes and heart attacks associated with the condition. The key is sticking to appropriate lifestyle measures and taking the prescribed medication. The problem with treating high blood pressure is that most affected people have no obvious symptoms requiring relief, and consequently many don't follow their doctor's instructions and take their medication.

HUNTINGTON'S DISEASE

An inherited genetic disorder which causes damage to parts of the brain, resulting in abnormal movements and impairment of intellectual functioning.

What are the causes?

This autosomal dominant disorder results in damage to tissue in the cerebral hemispheres, the parts of the brain that deal with intellectual functioning and movement control.

What are the symptoms?

These usually begin in middle age. The main features are chorea (sudden jerky movements), dementia (impairment of intellectual functioning) and changes in personality.

How is it diagnosed?

The diagnosis can usually be made from the symptoms but may be backed up by looking for certain abnormalities in the brain on CT scanning or MRI. DNA analysis can be used to confirm the diagnosis.

Family members may be tested for the gene abnormality, but are only offered DNA testing after genetic counselling.

What are the treatment options?

There is no specific treatment for the disease but drugs can help to control some of the problems it causes, such as chorea and depression, a common feature. Researchers are using injections of fetal tissue into the brain of laboratory animals in an effort to slow progression of the disease.

What is the outlook?

The disease is progressive. Affected individuals usually live for 10–20 years after the symptoms begin to develop.

HYPERLIPIDAEMIAS

A group of disorders in which the levels of particular types of fats (lipids) are raised.

These disorders can be categorised according to the types of lipid that are involved. Two major types of fat in the blood are cholesterol and triglycerides. In the disorder hypercholesterolaemia cholesterol levels are raised; hypertriglyceridaemia results when triglyceride levels are raised. In mixed hyperlipidaemia both are raised.

What are the causes?

These disorders can develop secondary to a variety of conditions, such as obesity, diabetes mellitus and excessive alcohol intake. They may also be the result of certain inherited disorders that affect the processing of lipids. These so-called primary hyperlipidaemias are the result of gene defects. A common example is familial hypercholesterolaemia.

Many people with a mild elevation of lipids probably have a predisposition to these conditions that is exacerbated by a high-fat diet.

What are the symptoms?

In familial hypercholesterolaemia there may be swellings on the eyelids (xanthelasmas) and under the skin (xanthomata). There may also be a white ring around the iris, the coloured part of the eye. Early coronary heart disease (CHD) can develop; those who have only one copy of the abnormal gene may develop symptoms such as chest pain in their 30s and 40s; those with two copies of the abnormal gene may develop CHD as teenagers.

Very high triglyceride levels can also cause crops of xanthomata and are associated with an increased risk of acute pancreatitis (inflammation of the pancreas).

How is it diagnosed?
These diseases may be picked up during a medical check-up that includes measurement of blood lipid levels, as the result of a family history, or if coronary artery disease develops at an early age.

What are the treatment options?
The first line of treatment is a diet that is low in cholesterol and saturated fats. Regular exercise is also recommended. If the levels remain elevated despite an appropriate diet and treatment of any underlying causes, treatment with drugs, such as statins, will be considered. In secondary hyperlipidaemias, the cause is treated where possible

What is the outlook?
In many cases it is possible to bring the lipid levels under control and so reduce the risk of early CHD. Adherence to the appropriate diet is an important part of the management.

HYPERTENSION
see High blood pressure (page 147)

INHERITED THROMBOPHILIA
A genetic defect causing coagulation disorders and the most common cause of venous thrombosis.

Normal blood clotting is a complex process involving the interplay of many protein factors in the blood. Genetic mutations in many of these factors can lead to abnormal clotting but one in particular (a mutation called factor V Leiden) is very common in the general population and contributes to common coagulation disorders such as venous thrombosis.

Factor V Leiden affects 5 per cent of the Caucasian population and 1 per cent of Afro-Caribbeans. This mutation increases the risk of venous thrombosis up to 8-fold in those who inherit one flawed copy of the gene and up to 140-fold for those who inherit two flawed copies.

What are the causes?
The cause is a change of a single base on the factor V gene: an A appears where there should be a G. This mutation occurs where factor V interacts with other blood proteins to regulate formation of a blood clot. The mutation prevents this interaction which results in abnormal clotting and risk of thrombosis.

What are the symptoms?
The condition can be symptomless until a clot forms. An early episode of venous thrombosis (before the age of 40), repeated pregnancy loss, pre-eclampsia or a stroke may be the first indication that a person has the defect. Many people with factor V Leiden remain healthy. The oral contraceptive pill increases the risk of venous thrombosis in those with the deficient factor.

Estimates suggest that as many as half of all cases of venous thrombosis occur in those with the factor V Leiden mutation.

How is it diagnosed?
It is suspected in those with a family history of venous thrombosis or other symptoms as above, but diagnosis is confirmed by DNA testing.

What are the treatment options?
Treatment is with blood products to boost the missing factors. Warfarin may be prescribed to thin the blood. Advice may be given on reducing the risk of thrombosis after surgery, for example, and while travelling or following a period of immobilisation. Contraceptive advice may also be offered.

What is the outlook?
The outlook is good for those who are correctly diagnosed and treated. However, many people with the defective gene do not know they have it until they suffer a thrombosis or other incident which prompts DNA testing.

KLINEFELTER'S SYNDROME
A chromosomal disorder affecting males in which an additional X chromosome is present.

What are the causes?
The normal pattern of sex chromosomes in males is XY, but in Klinefelter's syndrome the pattern is XXY. (Other chromosomal patterns – XYY, XXX, XXXY and XXXX– are found, but these are not Klinefelter's syndrome.)

What are the symptoms?

Symptoms don't usually become noticeable until around or after puberty. Affected boys are tall, with long slender arms and legs. They tend to have a small penis and small testes. There may be some swelling of the breast tissue. Boys with Klinefelter's are infertile or have reduced fertility due to a lack or absence of sperm. Testosterone levels are often low. Some affected boys have mild learning difficulties.

How is it diagnosed?

The condition may be suspected around puberty but may go undetected in some cases. It is confirmed by a blood test that analyses the sex chromosomes.

What are the treatment options?

Testosterone may be given with the aim of stimulating sexual development and preventing breast swelling.

What is the outlook?

Overall, the health prognosis is good; infertility is likely to be the main problem.

MARFAN'S SYNDROME

An inherited disorder of the connective tissue of the body that affects joints and may be associated with certain other complications.

What are the causes?

Marfan's syndrome results from a gene abnormality inherited in an autosomal dominant manner.

What are the symptoms?

Affected individuals are tall, with long limbs and long thin fingers and toes. There is great flexibility of joints and curvature of the spine may develop. There may also be eye problems. Problems affecting the cardiovascular system may develop, including heart valve disorders and an aneurysm of the aorta – a balloon-like swelling that develops in the artery carrying blood away from the heart, which may rupture.

Abraham Lincoln is believed to have had Marfan's syndrome.

How is it diagnosed?

Marfan's is usually diagnosed from an examination, but it may be confirmed by plotting a family history of the disease or by testing for the gene abnormality. The disorder sometimes arises spontaneously with no family history.

What are the treatment options?

The heart, eye and joints are monitored for problems, with appropriate treatment as they arise. Beta-blockers may be prescribed with the aim of slowing swelling of the aorta. Family members are offered genetic counselling.

What is the outlook?

The prognosis is greatly improved by looking for and treating cardiovascular problems early.

PHENYLKETONURIA

An inherited genetic disorder in which the lack of an enzyme can result in damage to brain tissue.

In phenylketonuria, there is a lack of the enzyme needed to break down phenylalanine, one of the amino acids the body needs to make up proteins. As a result, substances accumulate in the blood that can damage the developing brain.

What are the causes?

The abnormal gene is inherited in an autosomal recessive manner.

What are the symptoms?

If the condition is not treated, symptoms tend to develop during the first 12 months of life and may include vomiting and convulsions. A delay in normal mental development may also be noticed.

How is it diagnosed?

All newborn babies are screened for the condition by testing a tiny blood sample taken by pricking the heel.

What are the treatment options?

Babies are given a special milk that contains protein but not much phenylalanine. A diet that is low in foods containing phenylalanine – essentially high protein foods – must be followed. Fruit and vegetables and some cereals are supplemented with synthetic protein. Doctors used to relax this regime when a child reached their teens. but now suggest the diet should be followed indefinitely. The artificial sweetener aspartame must be avoided.

What is the outlook?

With early diagnosis and treatment, the prognosis is good. Without treatment, serious damage to the brain can occur, resulting in severe learning disabilities.

POLYCYSTIC KIDNEY DISEASE (PKD)
Characterised by the development of cysts within the kidneys, this inherited condition often causes kidney failure in middle age.

Polycystic kidney disease, inherited through a mutated autosomal dominant gene, is the most common form of kidney disease, affecting about 1 in 500 people. Cysts increase in size and number during the course of the patient's life, causing the kidneys to enlarge and eventually fail.

What are the causes?
Most cases of PKD are autosomal dominant. The mutation is in the gene polycystin 1, or occasionally polycystin 2. There is a less common form of PKD that is an inherited autosomal recessive disorder; this form can cause kidney failure in childhood.

What are the symptoms?
The cysts grow very slowly and there are often no symptoms until poor kidney function indicates that something is wrong. There may be blood in the urine. There may be pain if the kidneys are very enlarged and/or become infected, or if bleeding occurs within a cyst, or kidney stones develop.

How is it diagnosed?
Cysts may be detected by ultrasound, CT scanning or MRI. A diagnosis can usually be made in early adulthood. It is difficult to diagnose autosomal dominant PKD in children, when cysts are in the early stages of development, and because there is no specific treatment for early PKD, testing the children of affected parents is often not carried out until they have reached adulthood.

What are the treatment options?
PKD cannot be cured, nor the kidneys restored to normal condition. Complications such as high blood pressure and infection are treated as they develop. As the kidneys fail, uraemia (the build-up of waste products normally excreted in the urine) is treated and dialysis started. Transplantation is usually an option as long as a suitable donor kidney can be found. A polycystic kidney is only surgically removed if it causes chronic pain or there is persistent kidney infection.

What is the outlook?
With the introduction of dialysis and kidney transplantation, the outlook for the patient is good.

PROGERIA
An extremely rare genetic condition that produces rapid ageing in children.

Progeria is believed to be due to a mutation in a single dominant gene. Parents and siblings are not affected, so the mutation is thought to be sporadic, arising in the individual sperm prior to conception. It affects both sexes equally, and its incidence is reckoned at 1 in 4 million. Newborn babies appear normal, but within a year show a failure to grow. The characteristic appearance includes a small face and jaw relative to head size, pinched nose, baldness and aged-looking skin. Symptoms also include stiff joints, hip dislocation and cardiovascular problems. Intelligence is not affected. Diagnosis is made on physical appearance, but researchers are working on a genetic test.

Currently there is no cure; treatment aims to relieve symptoms – for example, surgery to ease cardiovascular problems. Few children survive beyond their early teens.

RETINITIS PIGMENTOSA
A group of inherited eye disorders characterised by progressive deterioration of the retina and consequent loss of vision.

What are the causes?
The conditions vary in severity and in the age of onset. Inheritance may be autosomal dominant (15 per cent of cases), autosomal recessive (80 per cent of cases) or X-chromosome-linked (5 per cent of cases, but in affected families 50 per cent of males will have the condition).

It is the rod cells responsible for vision in low light conditions and the pigment layer of the retina that are affected. Pigment accumulates in parts of the retina, and eventually there may be wasting of the optic nerve at the back of the eye.

What are the symptoms?
The first symptom is night blindness. The eye's visual field becomes restricted, but this is usually not noticed until the condition is advanced. By the age of 50 or so, many sufferers have poor vision.

How is it diagnosed?
A detailed family history is necessary. A visual field test shows progressive reduction of the field of vision, and the retina shows distinctive changes as dark patches of pigment

accumulate. Electrical recordings of eye movement and of the sensitivity of the retina to light will be taken.

What is the outlook?
No treatment can halt the progression of the condition, but low-vision aids can help with daily activities. The condition may progress to almost complete loss of vision.

SEVERE COMBINED IMMUNODEFICIENCY (SCID)
A disorder affecting babies that is caused by a lack of the white blood cells needed to fight infection.

What are the causes?
SCID is inherited and a number of variants exist. Sometimes the condition is X-chromosome linked, meaning that it is passed on from the mother, who is an unaffected carrier. Other cases show an autosomal recessive pattern of inheritance, when both parents carry the gene in recessive form. The abnormal gene that causes SCID affects proteins in the type of white blood cells known as T lymphocytes, which means that babies born with the condition have no 'T cells' in their immune systems with which to fight off viral, fungal and bacterial infections.

The world became aware of SCID in the 1970s through the story of David Vetter, a boy who lived all his life in a bubble. David died in 1984 at the age of 12 following a bone marrow transplant.

What are the symptoms?
Babies with SCID become ill very soon after birth. Because they have no T cells, they are vulnerable to the same range of infections as patients with AIDS. They develop infections and rashes and fail to put on weight.

How is it diagnosed?
A full blood count show low numbers of lymphocytes. This is followed by a T cell count, which in cases of SCID usually reveals that there are no T cells in the blood.

What are the treatment options?
Infants with SCID must be protected from infections. In the past this was done by isolating the child in a large plastic 'bubble'. Nowadays, patients are given regular injections of antibodies instead. If a compatible donor can be found, stem cell transplantation may be carried out. The variant of SCID that is X-linked and results from gamma chain deficiency can now be treated by gene therapy (see page 125).

SICKLE CELL DISEASE
A genetic disorder in which red blood cells become sickle-shaped and block the blood supply to tissues and organs.

In sickle cell disease, the structure of haemoglobin, the oxygen-carrying pigment in red blood cells, is abnormal and is known as haemoglobin S. When haemoglobin S releases the oxygen it is carrying, the haemoglobin molecules change shape and distort the red blood cells so they become sickle shaped. Unlike normal red blood cells, which are flexible and can squeeze through small spaces, these cells are stiff and so can block small blood vessels, depriving parts of the body of blood and oxygen. These cells may also be broken down earlier than they should be and this results in anaemia. People from in certain parts of the world, in particular tropical Africa, are at increased risk of the disease.

An individual with one abnormal copy of the haemoglobin-producing gene is said to suffer from sickle cell trait; a person with two abnormal copies is said to suffer from sickle cell disease.

What are the causes?
The inheritance pattern is autosomal recessive. People who carry one copy of the abnormal haemoglobin gene do not suffer any symptoms. However, they may require extra oxygen under anaesthetics or at high altitude.

What are the symptoms?
These may be noticed from around the age of six months. Sickling may be triggered by exercise, being at high altitude where the oxygen levels are low, infections and dehydration.

Sickling results in acute flare-ups of the symptoms, known as crises. Children often have pain and swelling in their fingers and toes which do not get enough blood and oxygen. In older patients, bone pain is the most common problem, but other symptoms may include chest pain, convulsions, blood in the urine and pain in the liver region. The features depend on the area of the body particularly affected. There may also be fever.

Possible long-term problems include susceptibility to infections, leg ulcers, gallstones, kidney disease, visual impairment and strokes. The severity of the condition varies between individuals.

How is it diagnosed?
A blood test, called haemoglobin electrophoresis, is used to diagnose those with the disease and also those who are

carriers of the abnormal gene. The condition can also be diagnosed prenatally by DNA testing.

What are the treatment options?
The disease cannot be cured, so treatment is aimed at controlling it and relieving symptoms. Pneumococcal vaccination and daily doses of the antibiotic penicillin aim to prevent certain serious infections. All infections require prompt treatment with antibiotics.

Acute attacks are treated with fluids, antibiotics, oxygen and painkillers. In the future, gene therapy may play a role in the treatment of sickle cell disease.

What is the outlook?
This depends on the severity of the disease. Some of those affected have few complications. However, complications of severe disease may prove fatal in the first few years of life.

SPINA BIFIDA
A developmental defect affecting the spinal cord and its surrounding tissue.

What are the causes?
The reasons why this neural tube defect occurs are still largely unknown. During embryonic development, the neural tube forms along the back of the embryo; the upper part forms the brain, the lower part the spinal cord. Both of these structures are covered by three layers of tissue known as the meninges.

If the neural tube does not close up properly, spina bifida may result. In this condition, the spinal cord and the meninges that cover it are exposed through a gap in the vertebral column. The severity of the defect varies (p. 118), as does its site on the spinal column. In spina bifida occulta there is only a minor defect in the vertebral column and this is covered by skin, sometimes associated with a tuft of hair or a dimple over the affected area. In rare cases, a neural tube defect affects the brain and skull and may be fatal.

What are the symptoms?
These vary depending on the severity of the defect. Spina bifida occulta is unlikely to cause any symptoms. However, in more severe cases of spina bifida there may be:
• weakness and numbness of the legs;
• problems with bowel and bladder control;
• paralysis.
Spina bifida may also be associated with hydrocephalus.

I have a child with spina bifida. I want another baby but can I be sure it won't happen again?
Spina bifida is multifactorial – there seems to be a genetic component, but environmental factors, notably a woman's folate status, also play a large part. The incidence of neural tube defects (NTDs) – spina bifida, in which the neural tube fails to close around the spine, and anencephaly, in which it fails to close around the brain – is of the order of 1 in 1000 in the general population. However, for women who already have had a child with an NTD, this rises dramatically to 1 in 20. Women who have a close relative who has had a child with an NTD are also at increased risk. The risk is about half and half for spina bifida or anencephaly, regardless of which condition affected the first child. Anencephaly leads to miscarriage or stillbirth or proves fatal within the first few days of life.

For anyone who has an increased risk of having a child with a neural tube defect, genetic counselling is available. This can provide up-to-date information, an assessment of an individual's particular risk, a preventive plan involving improving folic acid intake through supplementation, and a review of the prenatal screening tests which are available to detect affected babies before birth.

ASK THE EXPERT

How is it diagnosed?
A prenatal blood test is offered at about 16 weeks gestation to identify those women who have an increased risk of producing an affected baby, such as those who have already had a child with a neural tube defect. The detailed scan performed at around 20 weeks may be carried out earlier for a woman in whom a high risk has been identified. Babies born with spina bifida are likely to have CT scanning or an MRI shortly after birth to determine the severity of the defect.

What are the treatment options?
Taking folic acid before conception and for the first 12 weeks of pregnancy has been shown to reduce the risk of spina bifida and other neural tube defects.

In mild cases, no treatment is likely to be required. In severe cases, surgery will be performed on the defect where possible, and measures taken to drain the excess fluid from the brain if hydrocephalus is present.

Otherwise, treatment aims to alleviate the problems caused. This may include physiotherapy, advice on aids to maximise mobility and catheters for those with incontinence. The affected individual and the family will need support.

What is the outlook?
In milder cases, the prognosis is usually good. Severe cases result in permanent disability.

TALIPES
See Club foot (page 141)

TAY-SACHS DISEASE
A genetic disorder that causes damage to the central nervous system (the brain and spinal cord).

What are the causes?
Tay-Sachs disease is caused by a lack of an essential enzyme, hexosaminidase A. This leads to the accumulation of a fat, GM2 ganglioside, in the cells of the central nervous system, particularly in the brain, causing damage.

The inheritance pattern is autosomal recessive: when both parents are carriers there is a 25 per cent chance of having an affected child with each pregnancy. Various gene defects can cause the disease. Certain populations are at increased risk of carrying the abnormal gene, in particular Ashkenazi Jews from Eastern Europe and the French Canadians of southern Quebec.

What are the symptoms?
Symptoms are usually first noticed when a baby is a few months old, when apparently normal development begins to slow. Problems with vision and eventually blindness may develop. Later, there may be convulsions. From around the age of two, movement and coordination become problematic. Eventually there are problems with swallowing and breathing.

In some forms of the disease, the symptoms develop later in life, in the 20s or early 30s.

How is it diagnosed?
The diagnosis is made by blood tests, either through gene analysis or by measuring enzyme levels in the blood.

Gene analysis of blood samples to identify carriers can be performed for those in at-risk populations or those with an affected relative. Genetic counselling is also available. Because not all the gene defects have yet been identified, DNA analysis does not always pick up carriers, although it does so in most cases. This testing may, therefore, be backed up by measuring the enzyme levels. (Affected individuals have no hexosaminidase A enzyme in the blood and carriers have reduced levels.)

Tests, such as amniocentesis and chorionic villus sampling, can be performed prenatally to see whether a fetus is affected. A couple may wish to consider a termination if the test is positive – counselling should be offered before and after testing.

What are the treatment options?
There is at present no cure for the disease but extensive research is ongoing.

It may be possible to avoid having an affected baby by assisted conception techniques – either by artificial insemination, using sperm from a non-carrier donor, or by in vitro fertilisation, in which the developing embryos are tested before being implanted in the uterus to check that they do not have two copies of the abnormal gene. This is

---

Palliative care for children: the role of children's hospices

TALKING POINT

Living with a child with a life-limiting illness is emotionally draining and parents need a lot of support, as well as advice on practical care issues. Many conditions result in degeneration over some years, placing great stress on the whole family. Increasingly children's hospices are supporting families through their child's illness, treatment and death. This may include:

• Regular care breaks for children and their families in a relaxed nurturing environment.
• Emergency care as necessary.
• Physical, social, emotional and spiritual support.
• Community care for families, often around the clock
• Support for siblings.
• Terminal care for affected children, allowing their lives to end free from pain, and with dignity and calm.
• Bereavement counselling for parents and siblings and support through their grieving process.

Since so many life-limiting conditions, such as Tay-Sachs have a genetic component, some families may have more than one affected child and need extra help.

only possible when the parents have a recognised genetic abnormality so that the doctors know what to look for. This procedure is complex and costly and, as with all assisted conception techniques, there is no guarantee that it will be successful.

What is the outlook?
The main form of the disease is usually fatal in early childhood: very few children live beyond five, most die within the first two to three years. Research is, however, ongoing to find a treatment, and there are some options available to couples to avoid having a baby affected by the disease.

TURNER'S SYNDROME
A chromosomal disorder affecting girls, which in most cases results from an absence of the second female sex chromosome.

What are the causes?
Girls with Turner's syndrome usually have only one female sex, or X, chromosome rather than the usual two. In some cases, there is a chromosome mosaic in which some cells of the body have only one X chromosome and others have two or even three. The condition is thought to result from an abnormality of cell division in the embryo.

What are the symptoms?
Affected girls are short. The neck is short and they tend to have so-called webbing of the neck – wide skin attachment between the neck and shoulders – and widely spaced nipples. Their ovaries often fail to work properly, causing a reduced level or complete lack of the female sex hormones, oestrogen and progesterone. In most cases this will result in infertility.

There is an increased incidence of certain heart valve abnormalities and of narrowing of the aorta, known as coarctation. Affected girls are also at increased risk of high blood pressure in later life and of osteoporosis (thinning of the bones associated with an increased risk of fractures).

Girls with Turner's syndrome are usually of normal intelligence, but sometimes the condition is associated with mild learning difficulties.

How is it diagnosed?
The diagnosis is made from the examination and also by chromosomal analysis.

What are the treatment options?
Treatment may involve:
- Growth hormone supplements to encourage growth.
- Sex hormone supplements to stimulate sexual development and menstruation. (Giving oestrogen also reduces the risk of early osteoporosis.) Pregnancy may be possible through assisted conception techniques.
- Correction of congenital abnormalities, such as surgery for coarctation of the aorta.

What is the outlook?
With appropriate treatment, affected girls generally have a good prognosis and a normal lifespan.

VON WILLEBRAND'S DISEASE
An inherited disorder in which there is a deficiency of von Willebrand factor (vWF), which is needed for the blood to clot.

What are the causes?
The gene defect that causes von Willebrand's disease is usually inherited in an autosomal dominant manner, a dominant defective gene is passed on from one parent.

What are the symptoms?
The disease is generally mild, but its severity varies between individuals. Some have few problems, while others experience bleeding after minor injuries, easy bruising, nose bleeds and heavy periods.

How is it diagnosed?
Blood tests show reduced levels of von Willebrand factor and bleeding does not stop as quickly as it should. Clotting factor VIII, a lack of which causes a type of haemophilia (p. 146), may also be deficient.

What are the treatment options?
In mild cases no treatment is necessary. In other cases, the drug desmopressin may be given for bleeding episodes, or before tooth extraction or surgery, as this raises the levels of vWF and factor VIII.

If bleeding is severe, factor VIII concentrate may be given; this also contains von Willebrand factor.

What is the outlook?
The condition tends to be mild and amenable to treatment by the measures described.

Index

Acknowledgments

Carroll & Brown Limited would also like to thank:

Picture researcher
Sandra Schneider

Production manager
Karol Davies

Production controller
Nigel Reed

Computer management
Paul Stradling, Nicky Rein

Indexer
Jill Dormon

3-D anatomy
Mirashade/Matt Gould

Illustrators
Andy Baker, Rajeev Doshi at Combustion Design and Advertising, Kevin Jones Associates, Amanda Williams, John Woodcock

Layout and illustration assistance
Joanna Cameron

Photographers
Jules Selmes, David Yems

Photographic sources
SPL = Science Photo Library

1 Getty Images
7 Dept of Clinical Cytogenetics, Addenbrookes Hospital/SPL
8 *(top)* Alfred Pasieka/SPL
(top left) James King-Holmes/SPL
9 *(left)* SPL
(right) A Barrington Brown/SPL
10 Art Wolfe/SPL
11 *(right)* Rob Lewine/Corbis
(background) Alfred Pasieka/SPL
12 *(left)* Ted Horowitz/Corbis
(centre) Jon Feingersh/Corbis
(bottom) Peter M Fisher/Corbis
(background) Alfred Pasieka/SPL
13 James King-Holmes/SPL
15 Norbert Schaefer/Corbis
16 *(left)* Dr M A Ansary/SPL
17 *(top)* Biophoto Associates/SPL
27 Mitchell Gerber/Corbis
30 Dr Jeremy Burgess/SPL
31 *(top left)* Edelmann/SPL
(top right) SPL
(centre left, right)
Dr M A Ansary/SPL
(below left, right) Edelmann/SPL

(bottom left) Alex Bartel/SPL
(bottom right) Edelmann/SPL
32/33 Getty Images
36 Norbert Schaefer/Corbis
40 *(left, right)* Getty Images
42 *(left)* Getty Images/Allsport
(top right, bottom) Getty Images
43 Peltekian James/Corbis/Sygma
45 *(top)* Getty Images/Allsport
(centre) Getty Images
49 Getty Images
51 *(left)* Getty Images
(right, 4th, 5th from top) Getty Images
60 Getty Images
62 Getty Images
65 Getty Images
67 *(left)* imagesprite.com
(right) Getty Images
68/69 Getty Images
70/71 imagesprite.com
72 Getty Images
73 Getty Images
74 Getty Images
78 *(left)* Kevin R Morris/Corbis
(centre right) Getty Images
82 Kevin R Morris/Corbis
83 *(centre, centre right, bottom left)* Getty Images
87 Powerstock
90 Getty Images
92 *(left)* Dept of Clinical Cytogenetics, Addenbrookes Hospital/SPL
(centre) Peter Yates/SPL
(right) Biophoto Associates/SPL
93 Mauro Fermariello/SPL
99 C C Studio/SPL
103 *(top)* Yves Baulieu, Publiphoto Diffusion/SPL
(bottom) Faye Norman/SPL
104 *(top)* James King-Holmes/SPL
(bottom left, right) Dept of Clinical Cytogenetics, Addenbrookes Hospital/SPL
105 Saturn Stills/SPL
106 Mark Clarke/SPL
108 *(top)* James King-Holmes/SPL
(bottom) Chris Priest and Mark Clarke/SPL
109 *(left)* Will and Deni Mcintyre/SPL
(right) Peter Yates/SPL
110 Carroll and Brown
113 Tek Image/SPL
115 Will and Deni McIntyre/SPL
120/121 Birmingham Children's Hospital Medical Illustration
123 Ed Young/SPL

124 Biophoto Associates/SPL
127 J C Revy/SPL
128 Photo-Journalists International/ Corbis KIPA
129 Victor Habbick Visions/SPL
130 Rex Features
133 *(top)* Getty Images
(centre) Mauro Fermariello/SPL
(bottom) Getty Images
134 Lauren Shear/SPL

Front cover Digital Vision
Back cover *(centre)* Getty Images
(right) Mauro Fermariello/SPL

Contact details

Albinism Fellowship
www.albinism.org.uk

Association for Spina Bifida and Hydrocephalus
01733 555988
www.asbah.org

Cleft Lip and Palate Association
020 7431 0033
www.clapa.com

Cystic Fibrosis Trust
020 8464 7211
www.cftrust.org.uk

Down's Syndrome Association
020 8682 4001
www.dsa-uk.com

The Haemophilia Society
0800 018 6068
www.haemophilia.org.uk

Huntington's Disease Association
020 7223 7000
www.hda.org.uk

Multiple Sclerosis Society
0808 800 8000
www.mssociety.org.uk

Muscular Dystrophy Campaign
020 7720 8055
www.muscular-dystrophy.org

NHS Direct 0845 4647
www.nhsdirect.nhs.uk

Sickle Cell Society
020 8961 7795
www.sicklecellsociety.org

619–014–2